Stop Abusing Bernoulli!

How Airplanes Really Fly

Gale M. Craig

Regenerative Press
Anderson, Indiana

© Copyright 1997 Gale M. Craig

Published by:

Regenerative Press
1900 Romine Road
Anderson, Indiana 46011
FAX 765 643 0855

Printed and bound in the United States of America

Cataloging in Publication Data

Craig, Gale M., 1927-
Stop Abusing Bernoulli!-- How Airplanes Really Fly

Includes index.
1. Aerodynamics   2. Aeronautics
TL570.C735   1997   629.132'3

Library of Congress Catalog Card Number   97-91991

ISBN 0-9646806-2-9

Stop Abusing Bernoulli!
How Airplanes Really Fly

Preface

It is generally accepted that lift of a wing is produced through interaction with passing air. In explaining this interaction, the only known physical principles which credibly apply are Newton's second and third laws. With these, upward lift can be described as the force of reaction to the action of accelerating air mass downward. Thus one might reasonably expect lift of wings to be explained in a context of Newtonian action-reaction forces. However, aerodynamics publications normally found in libraries and bookstores hardly mention Newtonian principles, but center instead, with questionable reasoning, on the Bernoulli theorem.

A first, most popular and simplistic explanation of lift, requires a wing to have a more convex upper surface as compared to the lower. It does not allow for flight of rubber band powered models with flat wings, or inverted flight of aerobatic airplanes; and as we shall see, it cannot survive algebraic consideration in a simple application.

A second explanation, taught in colleges and universities, adopts electro-magnetic principles of *vorticity* and *induction*. Leakage of air around the wingtips is said to produce wingtip vortices which "*induce* downwash," causing an "*induced* angle of attack" resulting in "*induced* drag." Ground effect, the increase in wing efficiency when operating near the surface, is explained in terms of image wingtip vortices reflected in the ground which *induce* inverted downwash which partially cancels the real induced downwash. To initiate lift, the theory requires a sharp trailing edge to produce a first vortex which somehow causes, or *induces*, another around the wing. This teaching, like the first, begins with a wing shape character-istic (sharp trailing edge) that is in fact not required in the real world, and invokes fictitious inductive effects in air which have no basis in known physical science.

Magnetic vortices propagate at the speed of light, so that observed effects are relatively instantaneous. However, air vortices propagation involves air mass inertia and acceleration requiring much greater time. Thus induction theory taken from electromagnetism, in addition to being abused, is of little value in explaining transient phenomena involving air mass inertia, as in the momentary high level of lift associated with rapidly increased of angle of attack, or the repeating cycles of lift production, stall, and reversal of lift of a cylindrical form in passing flow.

It is said "to make an omelet one must break eggs." For us the omelet-to-be is an explanation of basic aerodynamic principles in terms of Newtonian physics. The eggs to be broken are those of traditional aerodynamics, which provide a wealth of information in experimental data and pictures traditionally explained in a context of electromagnetic principles. Perhaps this is because one of the early aerodynamics investigators, Hermann Helmholtz, did pioneering work in both hydro-dynamics and electromagnetism.

We shall re-interpret known aerodynamic phenomena in terms of New-tonian Physics, and add a bit of experimental information and reasoning. Upward lift will be explained, and calculated, as force resulting from downward acceleration of air. We shall avoid using the Bernoulli theorem, leaving it for an appendix related to instrumentation.

I wish to express appreciation to my wife, Kiku, who has endured my withdrawals into incommunicative study and writing, to the Experimental Aircraft Association for their Oshkosh and Lakeland conventions forums where I have been permitted to present this subject and refine its content in response to questions and comments received, to retired Chief Aerodynamicist of Boeing Aircraft, Mr. John Wimpress, for his constructive and encouraging comments at two of my Oshkosh presentations, and to Mr. Martin Ingleman-Sundberg, retired after thirty years as head of the low speed aerodynamics section of The Aeronautical Research Institute of Sweden, for reviewing my manuscript and suggesting improvements which I have incorporated.

Gale Craig
September 1997

CONTENTS

Stop Abusing Bernoulli! How Airplanes Really Fly

I. PROBLEMS OF POPULAR THEORY

At the time of this writing, mankind has been flying airplanes for nearly a century. Presumably the principles of airplane flight are well documented, and can readily be found by any interested person. Yet one who diligently searches libraries and bookstores for publications explaining basic flight principles will find that the vast majority of explanations do not conform to known principles of physics, and the most popular explanation of wing operation contradicts common sense and observed fact.

Consider the most widely held theory of flight, which we may call *hump theory*. It says that wings lift upward because they have upper surfaces which are more convex than are the lower surfaces. If this were true, then airplanes could not fly inverted, as they are seen to do at airshows, because the more convex side would be on the bottom. Despite this and other contradictory facts, the pollution of hump theory continues to be inflicted upon the minds of elementary school students, high school students, aircraft technicians and even pilots.

As we shall see, hump theory cannot survive mathematical consideration. Therefore it cannot be taught to aeronautical engineers who are expected to produce useful mathematical calculations. Instead, another explanation, which we may call *induction theory*, is presented in highly mathematical context. Although induction theory appears to produce useful numerical results, it is faulty in that it is based upon induction principles, like those of electromagnetism, which do not really apply to air. It is assumed that air vortices and magnetic vortices both behave according to the same "laws of vorticity." However, as we shall see, this assumption is flawed.

1

Forces potentially available for lifting or propelling an aircraft for aerial navigation include buoyancy, as in the case of ballooning, magnetic action involving The Earth's magnetic field, as speculated for UFOs, wind, rocketry, and acceleration of air mass to produce reaction force. For airplanes, buoyancy is a real part of lift, but is a very small part which is generally ignored, magnetic levitation is not realistically possible with current technology, wind is a real factor in flight but is not controllable, and rockets are inefficient at general aviation speeds. This leaves no practical force available for lift and propulsion other than through action-reaction in acceleration of air mass according to principles of Newtonian physics. We refer to this process as *aerodynamics.*

As examples of aerodynamic action-reaction, airplane propellers gain forward thrust in reaction to accelerating air mass rearward, and rotating wings of helicopters gain upward lift in reaction to accelerating air mass downward. Downward acceleration of air mass is likewise the means by which airplane wings lift upward.

Strangely, the action-reaction principle is hardly recognized, and is rarely mentioned in popular theories of flight. Instead, lift explanation is so firmly centered on the *Bernoulli theorem* that it might be likened to a religion. It is as if Bernoulli had descended from a mountain in biblical times carrying a stone tablet on which was engraved "$p + 1/2 \, \rho \, v^2 = $ constant," and saying *"Behold-- It is decreed that feathered two-legged creatures with flapping upper appendages, which scurry about on the ground in search of worms and insects, shall henceforth navigate the skies."*

Daniel Bernoulli (1700-1782), was not a biblical figure, but a Swiss physicist and mathematician. He produced his theorem, or equation relating velocity and pressure, not by divine process, but through simple application of Newtonian physics. The Bernoulli theorem is not at all mysterious or magical, but says simply that pressure and velocity in moving air are inversely related. As one increases the other decreases. The theorem does not specify a cause and effect relationship establishing that pressure change is caused by velocity change or that velocity change is caused by pressure change. It only specifies that the changes occur simultaneously.

2

Both hump theory and induction theory improperly assign cause and effect in describing aerodynamic lift as due to pressure difference caused by velocity difference. It can be quite logically argued that this reasoning is reversed, and velocity difference results from pressure difference.

After we consider shortcomings of Bernoulli based theories of lift we shall not have further need of the theorem. Instead we shall use basic Newtonian physics to develop more appropriate *recirculation theory* based on action-reaction principles.

For the reader who is interested, the Bernoulli theorem is developed, with applications described, in Appendix A.

Hump Theory

Hump theory is based upon logic and two widely held principles of air behavior. One is the Bernoulli theorem, which indicates that air pressure and velocity are inversely related. The other principle is that of equal transit time, which maintains that time for air passage over a wing upper surface is equal to the time for air passage beneath the lower surface. Let us consider what these principles mean as applied to a wing having a convex upper surface and a more flat lower surface.

The length of flow path over a more convex upper surface would be greater than the length of path beneath the lower surface, as indicated in Figure 1.1.

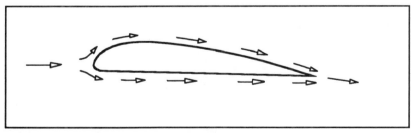

Figure 1.1 Wing With More Convex Upper Surface

A wing with a more convex upper surface would have a longer upper surface path for air flow as compared to the lower path.

If transit time for air passage over the longer upper surface is indeed equal to that beneath the lower surface, then upper surface velocity must be greater, in proportion to path length difference. Since the Bernoulli theorem says that if the upper surface velocity is greater than that of the lower, then pressure at the upper surface must be less than that at the lower, and we have an explanation of resulting upward force, or lift-- *if* the two basic premises are true.

There is no question as to the accuracy of the Bernoulli theorem, which is proven in many ways, including application to airspeed indicators. However, there is no proof to be found of the principle of equal transit times, according to which upper and lower surface flow velocities should be directly related to flow path lengths.

We can evaluate hump theory as it relates to flight data obtained in experiments with the author's airplane, shown in Figure 1.2. Pitot tubes are shown mounted on a vertical pipe attached to the Cessna 150 wing. Manometers in the right side window were used to read pitot tube differential pressures. The pitot tubes were moved vertically between flights to obtain pressures at one foot increments above and below the wing.

Figure 1.2 **Cessna 150 With Pitot Tubes**

Relative velocities, or indicated airspeeds, were measured along a vertical line six inches ahead of the wing leading edge. To measure velocities below the wing, the pitot mounting pipe was repositioned downward.

Dyed water manometers mounted in the airplane window were used to read pitot tube pressure differentials. Pitot pressure readings converted to relative flow velocity readings, or indicated airspeeds in feet per second, are indicated by the dots in Figure 1.3. Averaging airspeed readings of 99 and 120 feet per second at plus and minus five feet height gives airplane airspeed of 114.5 feet per second, or about 78 miles per hour.

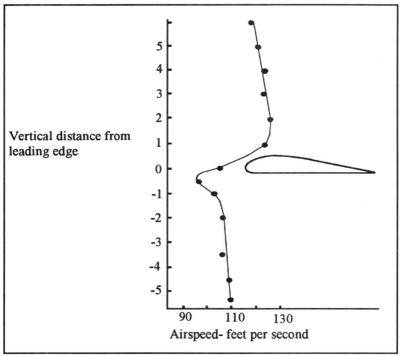

Figure 1.3 **Indicated Airspeeds Above and Below Leading Edge**

Indicated above and below wing airspeeds just ahead of the leading edge differ by about thirty percent. Farther back they would differ even more. If the principle of equal transit times is correct, then the Cessna 150 wing upper surface path must be more than thirty percent longer than that of the lower surface. However, actual measurement of the Cessna wing finds the upper surface path to be less than two percent longer than that of the lower.

5

If we were to design a wing with thirty percent greater distance from leading to trailing edge, it would have a quite radical profile perhaps like that of Figure 1.4. Obviously this is not like the wing in the Cessna photograph.

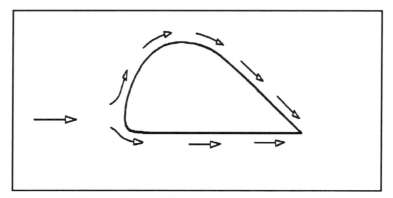

Figure 1.4 **Hump Theory Wing Section for a Cessna 150**

To have a thirty percent longer upper surface path length, a wing profile would have a quite unorthodox appearance.

It is easily calculated, through application of the Bernoulli theorem, what lift intensity would exist on a Cessna 150 wing at 80 miles per hour with a velocity difference of two percent. The result indicates that lift would be only slightly over one-half pound per square foot of wing area. This is but a small fraction of the rated wing loading of the Cessna, often pounds per square foot. Thus we have ample proof that hump theory is incorrect. The fault lies with the assumption of equal transit times. This assumption is false and has no basis in known principles of physics.

As further proof that hump theory is without merit, consider the wing profile of Figure 1.5, which will lift quite well, but has little room in its rear portion for structure of adequate strength to support aileron or flap mechanisms. On this section the upper surface path is shorter than the lower.

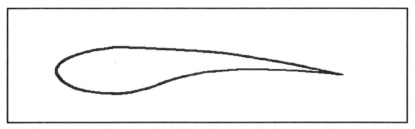

Figure 1.5 **Wing Section With Longer Path Lower Surface**

Through the years many have objected to hump theory. For example, in one of the most widely read books on flight, *Stick and Rudder*, copyrighted in 1944, Wolfgang Langwiesche says of hump theory: "Forget it. In the first place, Bernoulli's theorem does not really explain--the explanation is more puzzling than the puzzle!" He further says: "The main fact of heavier-than-air flight is this: the wing keeps the airplane up by pushing the air down." It would be better if he had used the word "accelerating" rather than "pushing," but the basic idea is correct.

In the November 1972 issue of *The Physics Teacher*, a five page article by Norman F. Smith, NASA aeronautical research scientist, described in detail the fallacy of hump theory. In his final paragraph he stated: "For explaining dynamic lift, the result of an encounter between a fluid and a lifting device, Newton's laws must be used.....Newton's third law is not only correct physics but also makes the whole business far easier to teach and to learn."

The problem is world-wide. In Sweden, Martin Ingelman-Sundberg, retired head of Low Speed Aerodynamics of The Aeronautical Research Institute of Sweden, has encountered much resistance in his attempts to reverse the spread of aerodynamic misinformation there, including official teachings of the "Swedish FAA."

Although hump theory is readily demonstrated to be false, and many have attempted to discredit and dispose of it, it continues to be included in books by highly respected publishers. For example, National Geographic published in 1996 a very nice book titled *Everyday Science Explained*. Overall, the book is worth its cover price of $35.00. However, it explains wing lift by saying that air flow over the top of the wing must travel faster than air flow beneath because "a wing's curved shape makes that part of the airstream travel farther in the same amount of time it takes air to pass underneath the wing." Then it invokes the Bernoulli theorem and the relationship of velocity and pressure. Another nice book, *The Way Science Works,* published around the same time by Macmillan, again describes wing operation with wording similar to that of the National Geographic book.

Since hump theory is readily shown to be false, one must wonder why it continues to be the foremost wing theory taught and published.

Possible answers include:

1. Because over the decades it has become so widely accepted that it is almost a religious belief.

2. Because it seems simple.

3. Because it is on FAA tests.

4. Because alternative college level induction theory is too mathematically complex for individuals not having a good calculus background.

5. Because induction theory, as taught in colleges and universities, is also flawed.

Perhaps item three is the most important. If FAA tests for pilot licenses are based on hump theory, flight schools must teach it. Item two is a factor--Theodore Von Karman, a most famous aerodynamicist, is reported to have said "When you are talking to technically illiterate people you must resort to the plausible falsehood instead of the difficult truth" (*Stories From a 20th Century Life*- W.R. Sears- Parabolic Press 1994).

Item four should not be a problem because, as we shall see, basic induction theory can be expressed in non-mathematical terms; and as to item five, flaws of induction theory will be considered as we proceed.

Half-Venturi Theory

Another sort of hump theory, not widely published, compares wing operation to a venturi tube. We may refer to this as *half-venturi theory*. As indicated in Figure 1.6, velocity of flow through a venturi tube is greater where flow converges in the smaller diameter portion.

Lower pressure exists in the more restricted, higher velocity flow, as the Bernoulli theorem would indicate. In a similar manner, wing upper surface flow is imagined to be caused to converge with increased velocity and lower pressure.

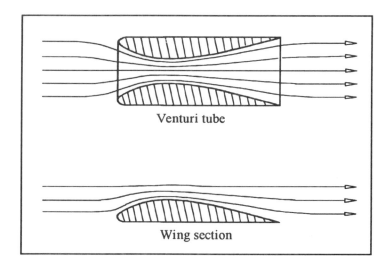

Venturi tube

Wing section

Figure 1.6 **Half-venturi Analogy of Wing Action**

A cross section of a venturi tube is illustrated in the upper figure, while a wing section is illustrated in the lower. Above the upper wing surface, flow streamlines are shown as squeezed upward as imagined in half-venturi theory. Flow velocity is thus said to be increased above the upper surface.

Half-venturi theory has the faults of hump theory, in not accounting for inverted airplane flight, the flight of balsa toy planes with flat wings, or flight of aerobatic planes having wings with equal upper and lower surface curvatures. In addition, the reasoning does not allow for differing flow velocities ahead of the wing, as was indicated in Figure 1.3.

Induction Theory

Aeronautical engineers are expected to develop understanding of wing operation in a mathematical context, so as to be able to produce numbers useful in aircraft design. Since hump theory, as we have seen, is proven false in numerical context, it finds no place in such higher education. Instead, at college level a different wing theory, which we may call *induction theory*, is taught in mathematical terms taken from studies of electromagnetism and electromagnetic induction.

It is perhaps unfortunate that mathematics of electromagnetic theory seems to fit so well into aerodynamics, for it is apparent that it has diminished the incentive for true understanding. This fit is partially because mathematical equations generally do not care about cause and effect. For example the Bernoulli equation relating pressure and velocity does not care which, if either, causes the other. Velocity change may be produced by pressure difference, as in an air stream issuing from a compressor, or pressure difference may be caused by velocity change, as in impact pressure rise at a surface intercepting the air stream.

Magnetic vortices around a wire are said to be *induced* by flow of electricity through the wire. In classical aerodynamic induction theory, which adopts the mathematics of electromagnetism, rotational movements of air are said to be induced by central vortex cores. Aside from viscous coupling, or drag, there is no basis in known physical science to support such an induction principle in air. It is more reasonable to state that rotational movements of air produce vortices.

If we push water rearward with a canoe paddle, vortices occur at the paddle edges. These are produced by forward recirculation of water from the higher pressure side of the paddle to the lower pressure side in response to pressure difference. In applying induction theory reasoning to the situation we would ignore acceleration of water mass around the paddle in response to pressure difference, and claim that water movement around the paddle is *induced* by the edge vortices.

This sort of perverse reasoning exists in college level induction theory because it is convenient for using the mathematics of electromagnetism.

Induction theory, like hump theory, explains lift in conjunction with the Bernoulli theorem, but difference in flow velocities at upper and lower wing surfaces is not attributed to a convex upper surface. Instead, velocity difference is said to result from flow over the *sharp trailing edge* of the wing. Never mind that a wing, as on the X-15, will fly well with a blunt trailing edge, or that sharpness of the trailing edge is masked by boundary layers. This is the basis of the induction theory of wing operation.

Flow over the sharp trailing edge is claimed to be the cause of a *starting vortex* which grows as it recedes behind the wing, as indicated in Figure 1.7. Creation and growth of the starting vortex is said to induce or cause creation and equal growth of *circulation* around the wing or airfoil.

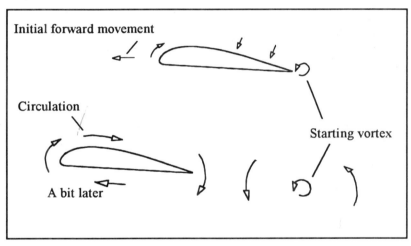

Figure 1.7 **Initial Movements Around Starting Airfoil.**

An airfoil beginning forward movement (upper figure) leaves a *starting vortex* behind and carries a *bound vortex* of *circulation* with it in forward movement. Starting and bound patterns grow simultaneously (lower figure).

This concept of circulation generation would appear to be in agreement with photographs of fluid movements around an airfoil shape by Ludwig Prandtl (1875-1953). These can be found in *Applied Hydro- and Aeromechanics,* by Prandtl and Tietjens. This and its companion volume, *Fundamentals of Hydro- and Aeromechanics*, available from Dover, both copyrighted in 1934, have become a sort of bible of aerodynamics upon which many other books are based.

11

Growths of the receding starting vortex and circulation around the airfoil are said to reach maturity after "a few chord lengths" of airfoil travel, whereupon circulation and lift stabilize. The starting vortex and circulation are real, but the *causes* as described are fictional.

Circulation, imposed upon passing flow, is said to cause the rise of oncoming air ahead of the wing, increase in rearward velocity of above wing flow, decrease of air velocity below, and downward departure of air at the rear. This is as it might be seen, if made visible, by an observer traveling with the wing or watching it in a wind tunnel.

A stationary observer watching wing passage would see relatively slow air movement ahead of the wing as rising, air above as moving rearward, air below moving forward and air at the rear moving downward. Taken altogether, these movements would comprise a closed circular path around the wing. Rising air ahead is sometimes termed *upwash*. We shall refer to descending air at the rear as *downwash,* although we shall later see that this term has other meaning in induction theory.

The two different perspectives, of a forward moving wing passing through still air, and a stationary wing in passing air, are combined in Figure 1.8 for comparison.

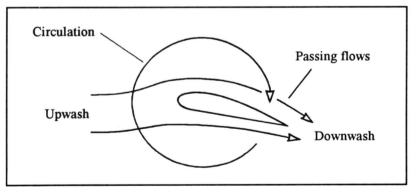

Figure 1.8 **Combined Flow Perspectives**

Instantaneous air movement around a passing wing, if visible, might be seen by a stationary observer as circular "circulation." Seen by an observer riding with the wing, approaching air would be perceived as rising in front, and departing air would be perceived as descending at the rear.

The two perspectives are both valid, since direction of movement is a subjective matter relative to the situation of whether the viewer is fixed in position relative to the wing or relative to undisturbed air.

Circulation, having strength represented by the symbol, Γ, tends to have vortex properties with velocity varying in inverse proportion to radius from the circulation center, as indicated in Figure 1.9.

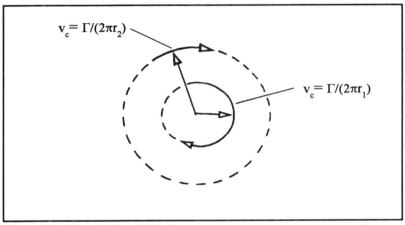

Figure 1.9 **Circulation Velocity**

Velocity of circulation around the circulation center tends to be inversely proportional to distance from the center. This is an important factor in computing lift. Relative circulation velocities at two radii are represented by lengths of the two curved arrows.

We can determine *circulation strength*, Γ (upper case Greek gamma), if we know circulation velocity, v_c, at some radius, r, as :

(1-1) $\Gamma = 2\pi r v_c$

Lift Calculation

By recognizing circulation, and describing circulation velocity distribution as being of vortex nature, induction theory establishes a useful foundation for lift calculation. In contrast, hump theory is useful only in deflecting questions of the curious about how wings work.

13

The concept of circulation and its relation to lift was put forward in two papers presented by Frederick William Lanchester, a successful automobile manufacturer, to two leading scientific societies of England in 1895 and 1897. Unfortunately, Lanchester's papers were rejected by these societies, and he was told that he should quit dabbling in the subject of flight, which was "merely the dream of madmen."

Still Lanchester persevered, and in 1907 and 1908 he published two books on aerodynamics which were well received, but this was at a time when successful manned airplane flight had been achieved and there was much interest in the subject.

Lanchester was not a college graduate, but learned much about physics and engineering principles through self-study. He invented many features of automobile mechanisms and engines which are still in use today, but his real interest was in flight. He contributed ideas on flight stability, skin friction, flat spins, propellers, aspect ratio and thermal soaring, but his most significant concept was that of the vortex theory of flight which became the foundation for the work of Prandtl and others.

The Kutta-Joukowski Theorem

An equation for lift of a cylinder in circulation of arbitrary strength was derived on the basis of the Bernoulli theorem through efforts of two men, M.W. Kutta (1867-1944) and N.E. Joukowski (1847-1921). This equation, known as the *Kutta Joukowski Theorem,* is:

$$(1\text{-}2) \qquad\qquad \text{Lift} = \rho v S \Gamma$$

where ρ is air density, v is airspeed, S is cylinder axial span and Γ is circulation strength.

The Kutta-Joukowski theorem applies to wings or airfoils as well as cylinders, but is only of academic value without knowledge of what determines circulation strength. Kutta theorized that circulation strength would automatically adjust to the level where airfoil upper and lower surface flows would merge smoothly at the trailing edge. This condition of smooth mergence is known as the *Kutta Condition.*

14

To make a complete lift equation, we can reason that factors which must be included in Γ are airspeed (because aerodynamic forces are proportional to airspeed squared), wing geometry and angle of attack, as defined in Figure 1.10. With circulation, oncoming air flow ahead of a wing is in a somewhat upward direction, as upwash, rather than straight on. As flow passes the wing it curves from rising upwash to descending downwash. If the wing is curved to accommodate flow curvature, it operates more efficiently. This curvature is known as *camber*. It has been found that curvature of the upper surface is more important than that of the lower, hence wings tend to have more flat lower surfaces, except on aerobatic airplanes which must fly well in inverted attitude.

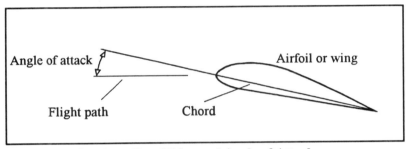

Figure 1.10 **Camber, Chord Line and Angle of Attack**

Camber is overall airfoil curvature effected by curvatures of upper and lower surfaces. The wing chord is a line from trailing edge to farthest point on the leading edge. The angle of attack is the angle between the chord line and flight path relative to the air. For an airfoil having mirror image upper and lower surface curvatures, the chord line would be a line of symmetry equidistant from the two surfaces.

Airfoil performance data is specified in terms of angle of attack; hence this angle is of some importance. The angle of attack is defined to be the angle between chord line and flight path relative to the air. For a symmetric airfoil, or one with no camber, zero lift coincides with zero angle of attack. For a cambered airfoil this is not true.

We shall not be concerned at this point with details of how induction theory arrives at an expression of circulation strength yielding smooth mergence, for we shall not be using the process. For an uncambered airfoil the strength is simply expressed as:

(1-3) $$\Gamma = \pi v C \sin \alpha$$

where C is wing chord, v is airspeed and α is angle of attack.

According to Prandtl's theory, circulation level adjustment would involve the starting vortex. Growth of the starting vortex would result from non-smooth mergence of flows at the airfoil trailing edge. Starting vortex growth would cause equal circulation growth until smooth mergence of flows would be achieved with stable vortex and circulation strengths.

Substituting circulation strength, Γ, from (1-3) into the Kutta-Joukowski equation, (1-2), yields:

(1-4) $$\text{Lift} = \pi \rho v^2 SC \sin \alpha$$

Since the product SC, or span times chord is rectangular wing area, we may rewrite the lift equation for an uncambered airfoil as:

(1-5) $$\boxed{\text{Lift} = \pi \rho v^2 A \sin \alpha}$$

where A is wing area.

This theoretical lift with no losses correlates well with wind tunnel test results at low angles of attack. Real world wings outside of wind tunnel confinement produce lift somewhat less than what the equation would indicate because of losses we shall consider.

As an application of the Kutta-Joukowski theorem, let us consider the Cessna 150 data found earlier in Figure 1.3. Since the data should be more accurate at points at more nearly vertical positions in relation to the circulation center, let us choose the data from positions of plus and minus five feet.

At the plus and minus five feet distances, indicated airspeeds differ from that of the airplane by about 5.5 feet per second, indicating that circulation

16

velocity at a radius of five feet is approximately 5.5 feet per second. Thus, from equation (1-1), Γ would be about:

(1-6) $\Gamma = 2\pi$ x 5ft x 5.5ft per second = 173 ft^2/second

Inserting this into the Kutta-Joukowski equation, with air density taken to be .0024 slug/ ft^3, airspeed 114.5 feet per second (78 mph), and wingspan 33 ft, yields lift of :

(1-7)   Lift = ρvSΓ
         = .0024 slug/ ft^3 x 114.5 ft/sec x 33 ft x 173 ft^2/sec
         = 1566 pounds

Considering that losses are associated with air movements around wing ends from higher pressure below to lower pressure above, and that the positions of circulation measurement may not have been ideal for representing mean effective circulation velocities, this result is remarkably close to the 1600 pounds rated gross weight of the Cessna 150.

Cause and Effect

Although test results correlate with induction theory, this does not prove validity of the theory, which begins with the unfounded premise that the trailing edge vortex causes circulation to appear around the wing. Like the assumption of equal upper and lower surface transit times, there is no justification in known principles of physics for such an effect. As we develop recirculation theory in a later section we shall reason that circulation is not produced by the starting vortex, but instead, the starting vortex and "circulation" are both produced by downwash *recirculation.*

Hump theory, half-venturi theory and induction theory all consider pressure difference and lift as resulting from flow velocity difference, and each provides different unsound explanations of why velocities differ. Actually it is more logical to describe velocity difference as resulting from pressure difference, in reversal of the popular concepts.

17

It is common knowledge that air accelerates from higher to lower pressure. Thus oncoming air flow naturally accelerates rearward into the lower pressure above-wing region and decelerates in passing into opposing higher below-wing pressure, as indicated in Figure 1.11. Thus above and below wing velocities are caused to differ because of pressure differences. Induction theory and hump theory manage to overlook these facts which do not fit into the Bernoulli theorem explanation of lift.

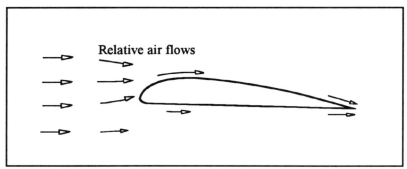

Figure 1.11 **Air Accelerations in Pressure Change Transit**

As indicated by the arrows representing flow, air is accelerated rearward and into the above-wing pressure region. Passing into the below-wing higher pressure region, velocity is reduced. Approaching the trailing edge, pressures and velocities revert to leading edge levels.

Why No Feedback?

It is clear that hump theory is totally without merit. However, we may assume that virtually everyone who has studied aerodynamics in college has previously been taught at a lower level that wing lift is in accordance with hump theory. One must wonder why the more educated multitudes have not bothered to return and enlighten the lower level education system with fundamentals of induction theory, which could easily be expressed in non-mathematical terms. Perhaps it is because of a general realization that induction theory is also faulty.

Higher level aerodynamics seems to be the domain of mathematicians, rather than physicists or engineers who might want to base the theory on sound principles. Perhaps we can trace the emphasis on mathematics with minimal regard for physical reality to interpretation of a statement by Lord Kelvin (1824-1907), who said "When you can measure what you are talking about and express it in numbers you know something about it. But when you cannot measure it or express it in numbers, your knowledge is of a meager and unsatisfactory kind."

Lord Kelvin was a brilliant scientist, but not all-knowing. He also stated in 1896: "I have not the smallest molecule of faith in aerial navigation other than ballooning."

We shall, in following sections of this book, develop more logical concepts to replace faulty hump and induction theories. In the process we shall reverse popular assignments of cause and effect, and describe velocity differences as due to pressure differences. In doing so we must provide an alternate explanation how the pressure differences are produced. This is not a real problem, for we can develop a quite logical explanation if we begin with the thoughts of Sir Isaac Newton (1642-1727), and add a bit of later knowledge and reasoning.

Sir Isaac Newton (1642-1727)

Stop Abusing Bernoulli!
How Airplanes Really Fly

II. A NEWTONIAN PERSPECTIVE

Newton's Lift Calculation

Although not widely recognized for pioneering work in aerodynamics, Sir Isaac Newton's contributions to the field are of the greatest importance. Newton provided a great portion of the understanding of physics and accompanying mathematics which we use today in aerodynamic and aeronautical work. Students begin with Newton's three laws of motion, which may be stated as:

1. A body at rest will remain at rest, or a body in motion will continue in straight line motion unless subjected to an external applied force.

2. When subjected to an external force the body will accelerate at a rate equal to the applied force divided by mass of the body.

3. The body will resist acceleration with force equal and opposite to that applied to it.

These most basic laws of physical science reflect the inertia of mass. The body of mass may be solid, as in the case of the moon, or it may be fluid, as water or air. It may even be an atomic particle such as an electron.

Newton was interested in flight, and made (considering the state of knowledge at the time) a quite logical attempt to produce an equation for aerodynamic lift. He considered an imaginary flat plate held at an angle of inclination relative to passing air flow, as indicated in Figure 2.1. Today we would call this angle the *angle of attack.* According to the laws of Newtonian physics, upward lift on the plate would be equal to the rate of downward momentum produced in downward deflection of flow. We shall be referring to this deflected flow as *downwash.*

In following the plate, the angle of flow deflection would be equal to the angle of attack. For small angles, where for practical purposes the angle in radians and its sine are equal, the vertical velocity component at the plate trailing edge can be considered equal to incoming air velocity times sine of the angle of downward deflection. This assumption is still valid today. However, Newton's concept of air behavior was incomplete, and as a result his lift calculation was lacking in accuracy.

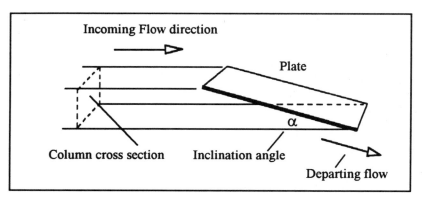

Figure 2.1 **Newton's Flat Plate**

Newton imagined that an inclined flat plate held in a horizontally flowing stream of air would intercept and deflect the column of air directly ahead of the plate. The column vertical cross section area would equal plate area times sine of the angle of inclination. Deflecting the stream of air downward would produce upward lift force equal to the rate of production of downward momentum, and would produce drag equal to the rate of rearward momentum reduction. No allowance was made for viscous, frictional or edge losses.

Calculations based on the foregoing considerations, involving high school physics, logic and algebra produce:

$$\text{Lift} = \rho v^2 A \sin^2\alpha \qquad \text{Drag} = \rho v^2 A \sin\alpha \ (1-\cos a)$$

where ρ is air density, v is airspeed, A is plate area, and α is the angle of attack; or since the plate is uncurved, α is also the angle of downwash. The drag, associated with rearward momentum reduction, would correspond loosely to what is currently called *induced drag*, and does not include other losses.

22

If Newton had tried designing a tow-launched glider based upon the above equations, he might have contemplated that:

1) With no child labor laws he might get a ten year old lightweight pilot.
2) As a first guess, total weight of plane and pilot reasonably might be about 400 pounds.
3) A horse-drawn tow into a wind might produce forty miles per hour airspeed.
4) Considering bird flight, a downwash angle of ten degrees would seem reasonable.

Solving for plate area, given the lift equation and above conditions, produces a huge minimum plate or wing area of 1600 square feet. Obviously, Newton's concept did not include all pertinent factors. Some individuals in later years blamed Newton for delaying manned flight by the discouraging nature of his conclusions.

So where did Newton go wrong? One of the factors overlooked by Newton was *surface attachment*, or *Coanda effect*, illustrated in Figure 2.2.

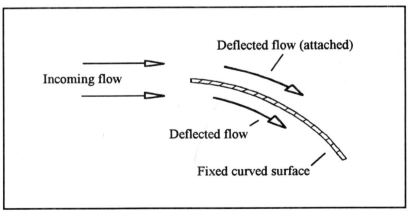

Figure 2.2 **Surface Attachment or Coanda Effect**

Coanda found that air flow is not only deflected by a surface upon which it directly impacts, but may also bend, or *attach*, as necessary to follow a convex surface which curves away from the initial direction of flow.

This oversight is understandable since Henri Coanda (1885-1972), who discovered surface attachment, was not yet born in Newton's time. If we add Coanda effect to Newton's concept, as indicated in Figure 2.3, the rate of mass deflection will be increased. Conceivably, if the downward momentum production rate were doubled, then the wing or plate area could be halved to 800 square feet. This would still be quite a large area, not in conformance with present-day experience.

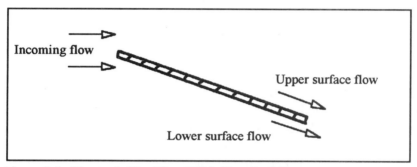

Figure 2.3   **Newton's Flat Plate With Coanda Effect**

With surface attachment, or Coanda effect, flow over the upper surface of Newton's flat plate would also be deflected to the direction pointed by the trailing edge. Downwash from the upper surface would merge at the rear with that from the lower surface.

Another factor is that downward deflection of a rectangular column of air would cause vertically adjacent air well above and below plate the to also be deflected, as indicated in Figure 2.4. Thus wing or plate area might be reduced further, but there remains one more important factor unrealized by Newton, and generally not addressed even today in descriptions of aerodynamic principles--- that of *recirculation,*.

Recirculation

All heavier-than-air aircraft maintain altitude in defiance of gravity by accelerating air mass downward. Upward lift force, which must support the aircraft weight, is equal to the downward rate of momentum change. Since compressibility of air is negligible in typical general aviation flight, downward displacement of air results in essentially equal upward recircu-

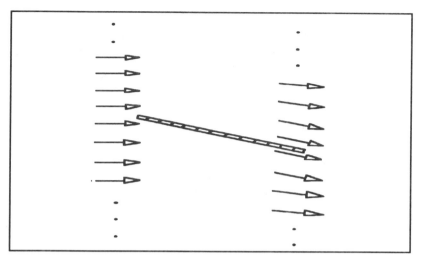

Figure 2.4 **Adjacent Flows Deflection**

As incoming air is deflected by passing in close proximity to Newton's flat plate, vertically adjacent air is also forced to be deflected. The mass deflection rate is thus much greater than Newton had imagined, and likewise, the lift pressure differential between upper and lower surfaces is also greater.

lation wherein space vacated above the airplane by downward air movement is refilled by outward, upward and then inward return movement of air displaced below.

Recirculation can be witnessed at airshows where twin rotating vortices left behind airplane wings are made visible by smoke. Unseen, but equal in intensity, is forward and upward recirculation into *upwash* ahead of the wing, as indicated in Figure 2.5. Like in the trailing vortices left behind, forward recirculation operates in a complete circuit of downward, forward, upward and rearward movement around the wing.

In induction theory, this forward circuit of movement is known as *circulation*, and is said to be the *source* of pressure difference and lift, but in reality the movement is *caused* by pressure difference created through downwash production. Ahead of the wing, air accelerates from below wing level forward and upward, and then rearward above wing level, in response to greater pressure below and reduced pressure above.

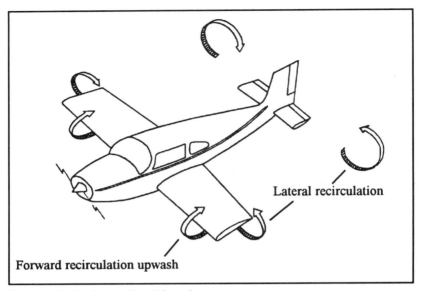

Figure 2.5 **Recirculation Directions**

Air accelerated downward by a passing airplane wing produces outward, upward and inward movement so that vacated space above is refilled from displacement below. The driving force for recirculation is the lift pressure differential where pressure is reduced above the wing and is increased below. Lateral recirculation is left behind in trailing vortices while forward recirculation produces rising *upwash* which is continuously recycled into the lift process as it is intercepted by wing forward movement.

Recirculation intensity, which varies with loading and in inverse relation to airspeed, is the basis of operation of a common stall warning device, illustrated in Figure 2.6. A stall warning switch actuator tab is located on the lower leading edge of many light airplane wings.

Recirculation is the final factor missing from Sir Isaac Newton's lift concept. Because of recirculation, which is actually unavoidable in subsonic flight, a lifting wing or flat plate like that of Newton continuously intercepts an updraft, or upwash, of its own creation. As the upwash is intercepted, the kinetic energy recovered is of great importance to lift efficiency. Downwash energy is continuously converted into upwash energy which is returned to the process. We may speak of the lift process as being a *regenerative* one in the sense that the downwash by-product, except for the portion lost laterally, is recycled into regenerating more lift.

Figure 2.6 **Stall Warning Switch**

When upward recirculation movement overcomes the downward spring loading on a stall warning switch tab, the tab moves upward and triggers an audible warning signal in the cockpit to inform the pilot that stall is near.

In summary, important factors unrealized by Newton were surface attachment, adjacent flow deflection and recirculation upwash recovery. Being unaware of recirculation, he was also unaware of lateral losses.

In airfoil section testing, lateral loss is prevented by confining the section in a wind tunnel where the test section, or airfoil, spans fully across the tunnel to contact the walls at each side, as represented in Figure 2.7. A real tunnel would be much larger in relation to airfoil chord than shown in the illustration in order to minimize interference effects.

Lift According to Newtonian Principles

Though based on questionable science, the lift equation of induction theory in the previous section is valid for the situation of no end losses, as in wind tunnel testing. An accurate lift expression including end loss effects would be beyond the scope of this book, but we can develop the equation for lift without losses from more sound scientific principles.

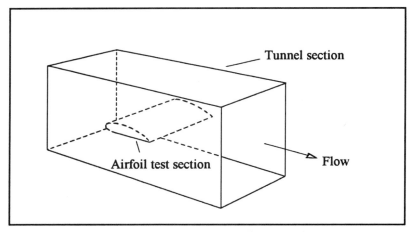

Figure 2.7 **Wall-to-Wall Wind Tunnel Airfoil Section Test**

The above illustration illustrates the mounting of a uniform airfoil section in a wind tunnel with airfoil ends in contact with the tunnel walls so as to prevent lateral air movement around the ends from higher pressure below to lower pressure above. An actual test would have tunnel dimensions much larger as compared to the airfoil in order to minimize interference effects.

From basic Newtonian physics, force is equal to the rate of change of momentum. The simplest expression of this is $F = ma$, or force equals mass times acceleration. For our consideration, upward force is equal to the rate of downward acceleration of air mass. This includes the rate of downward momentum production in downwash plus the rate of upward momentum interception in recirculation upwash. In a lossless situation where there is no lateral loss into trailing vortices, we need only to calculate the rate of downward momentum production in downwash and double the result to include equal upward momentum recovery in upwash.

Development of the lift equation is accomplished in Appendix A through calculation of the rate of downwash momentum plus an equal rate of return upwash momentum, as would occur in lossless conditions. The result is:

(2-1) $$\text{Lift} = \pi \rho v^2 A \sin \theta$$

In the foregoing expression, ρ is air density, v is airspeed, A is airfoil area, and θ is the downwash angle at the trailing edge. This is valid for any airfoil whether cambered or not, but airfoil performance data is normally given in terms of angle of attack. For an uncurved airfoil, or one without camber, the downwash angle at the trailing edge, θ, is equal to the angle of attack, α. Thus in terms of angle of attack, the lift of an *uncambered airfoil only* would equivalently be, as in induction theory:

(2-2) $$\text{Lift} = \pi\rho v^2 \, A \sin \alpha$$

In the general case, where an airfoil may or may not be cambered, the downwash angle is equal to the increase of angle of attack from that of zero lift where there is no downwash. The downwash angle then is equal to the angle of attack minus, α_0, the angle of attack for zero lift, and equation (2-1) above becomes:

(2-3) $$\boxed{\text{Lift} = \pi\rho v^2 \, A \sin (\alpha - \alpha_0)}$$

where α is angle of attack and α_0 is angle of attack at zero lift. This angle, $(\alpha - \alpha_0)$, is sometimes called the *absolute angle of attack*.

For the tunnel-confined lift curves of Figure 2.8, theoretical lift of the uncambered airfoil is represented by the straight line. Although, at higher angles, flow cannot accurately track the theoretical line, it can be seen that the lift equation is accurate at low angles. The failure of lift to faithfully conform to theoretical levels at higher angles of attack is due to viscous effects which we shall consider later.

The data plots show validity of the lift equation, whether it was derived through application of Newtonian physics, or through induction theory with invocation of the Bernoulli theorem, the Kutta-Joukowski theorem and the Kutta condition. Although the induction theory process was useful in finding a lift equation, cause and effect reasoning involving the Bernoulli theorem was reversed. Induction theory reasoning has also been convoluted a bit in applying the Kutta condition, which involves a sort of induction between starting vortex and circulation without justification in legitimate physics.

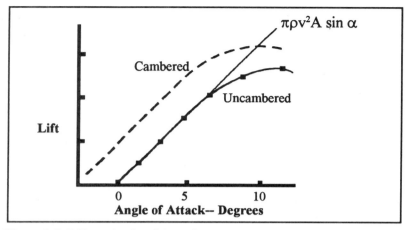

$$\pi\rho v^2 A \sin \alpha$$

Cambered

Uncambered

Lift

Angle of Attack-- Degrees

0   5   10

Figure 2.8 **Lift vs Angle of Attack**

Without camber the angle of downwash at low angle of attack is equal to the angle of attack. Thus lift plots along the theoretical ($\pi\rho v^2 A \sin \alpha$ line). A cambered lift curve is offset because of the way in which chord line and angle of attack are defined.

Kutta Reconsidered

Kutta theorized that the level of circulation around a wing would automatically adjust to a level such that flows would merge smoothly at the trailing edge. It was maintained that when this condition was reached, growth of the starting vortex would cease and consequently the simultaneous growth of circulation would cease. Some texts state that this condition is reached within a few chord lengths of wing travel.

Let us consider the relationship of circulation and the starting vortex. There is no reasonable explanation of their creation other than by recirculation of air from higher pressure beneath the wing toward lower pressure above. If we accept the idea that recirculation growth ceases within a few chord lengths of travel, this brings up new problems. Upward lift can only be properly explained as due to downward acceleration of air mass. If lift continues, then downward acceleration of air mass must continue, but downward acceleration is resisted by surrounding air mass, so that recirculation growth must continue. Thus circulation growth should never cease.

If downwash and recirculation growth continue forever, then it can be reasoned that lift increase grows with it. Does this mean that lift would become infinite? No; the lift equation derived from Newtonian momentum considerations assumed recirculation extending to infinity. Thus it reflects maximum possible lift.

This leads to a question of how lift can seem to stabilize while downwash and recirculation continue to expand. To answer this, a calculation of lift associated with air mass acceleration occurring within a few chord lengths (see page 134), finds that this accounts for most of the lift. The energy input rate to expanding circulatory movement would decrease as radius increases, and although never in theory becoming zero, it would become insignificant as upwash energy recovery approaches equality with downwash energy expenditure.

The foregoing, of course, considers only two dimensional air movements with no lateral loss. Two dimensional calculations to infinity correlate well with two-dimensional wind tunnel performance where confined downwash energy expenditure is equal to upwash energy recovery, except for losses to viscosity and turbulence.

In calculation of lift through Newtonian considerations of mass acceleration and reaction, we assumed a trailing edge downwash direction established by flow attachment, or Coanda effect. This in turn established recirculation strength. Thus we reversed cause and effect reasoning as compared to induction theory, which disregards Coanda effect, and says that attachment of flows at the trailing edge is brought about by circulation level adjustment, resulting from action of the starting vortex.

Accelerative Pressure Gradients

When air or other fluid is accelerated, a pressure gradient is produced which is opposite in direction to that of acceleration. As well known examples of pressure gradient production through acceleration, consider hurricanes and tornados. Both consist of air in circular motion where acceleration is centripetal, or center directed. Resulting centrifugal pressure gradients are outward from the centers. At the outside of a hurricane or tornado, pressure is that of a normal atmosphere, but at the center, pressure is reduced. In both cases, the low center pressures result from outward centrifugal pressure gradients which offset atmospheric pressure. Centrifugal pressure reduction in a tornado is known to be sufficient to cause buildings to explode from internal atmospheric pressure. Flow need not be completely circular to produce an outward pressure gradient. A gradient can be produced in simple curving flow.

As air is accelerated downward by passage over the downward curving slope of the upper surface of a wing, the resulting centrifugal pressure gradient is upward, as indicated in Figure 2.9.

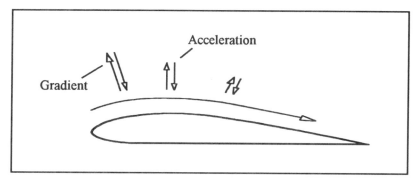

Figure 2.9 **Upper Surface Accelerative Pressure gradient**

As air is accelerated downward in following the airfoil upper surface, an upward centrifugal pressure gradient is developed which offsets atmospheric pressure to produce upper surface pressure reduction and lift.

Since downwash and recirculation encompasses the airfoil, one might wonder why centrifugal pressure drop is not uniform all around the section so that there is no net lift. Actually, in fore and aft directions, the pressure reduction forces indeed tend to be equal. At the front of the airfoil exists a centrifugal pressure drop known as "leading edge suction." This suction produces important forward thrust. At the rear, centrifugal pressure drop produces rearward thrust, or drag. With total downwash recycling and no frictional effects, forward thrust would exactly offset rearward thrust.

Although forward and rearward thrusts produced by centrifuging of air movement are in opposition, vertical forces reinforce because forward motion of the wing and accompanying recirculation center produces differing effects above and below the wing, as illustrated in Figure 2.10.

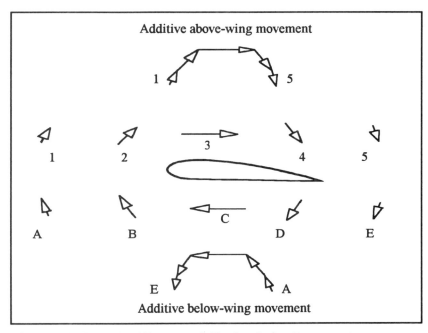

Figure 2.10 **Integrated Downwash-Recirculation Increments**

Directions of air movement during airfoil or wing passage are indicated by the numbered and lettered arrows. Numbers 1 through 5 indicate above wing movement, and letters A through E indicate movements below. Sequential additive connection of movements indicates that total motion as the airfoil passes is convex upward in both cases, meaning that acceleration is downward. Note that air movement below is actually counter-clockwise.

As the wing passes, actual movements of air involve downward acceleration both above and below the wing, with upward centrifugal pressure gradients as indicated by upwardly convex additive movements shown above. Thus upward lift is contributed by air movements both above and below the wing.

The Recirculation Energy Cycle

Energy can not be created or destroyed, but in interaction between moving masses, kinetic energy can transfer from one mass to another. This basic principle of physics applies to wings and airfoils in reaction with air, as illustrated in Figure 2.11.

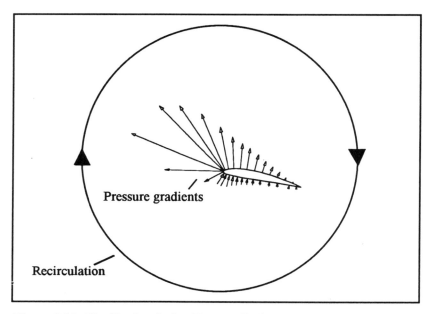

Figure 2.11 **The Recirculation Energy Cycle**

Energy is continuously transferred between a lifting wing or airfoil and the air circulating around it. Where the surface moves in the direction of aerodynamic force imposed upon it, kinetic energy of recirculation is absorbed in work of aiding airfoil movement. Where the surface is moving in a direction opposite to imposed thrust, energy flow is from the wing or airfoil to downwash and recirculation. The vectors indicate relative magnitudes and directions of pressure gradients around the airfoil surface, and also indicate directions and concentration of surface thrust.

The process of energy transfer between wing and moving air operates continuously in flight. Air recirculating around a wing or airfoil possesses kinetic energy derived from acceleration in interaction with the wing. As a wing moves forward in the direction of thrust imposed by leading edge suction, it absorbs energy from recirculation. This energy is transmitted to the airplane to assist forward movement. In turn, forward wing movement in opposition to rearward thrust requires energy input from the airplane, and so adds energy to recirculation. In a lossless situation these rates of energy absorption and expenditure would be equal so that there would be no net loss or drag. Aerodynamic force would be exactly perpendicular to the flight path.

The same principle applies in climb and descent. In climb, recirculation energy is absorbed as the wing moves upward in response to upward lift force. To maintain airspeed this expenditure of energy must be made up with increased angle of attack, which increases rearward thrust, so that engine thrust must be increased in compensation.

In sinking descent, gravitational work on the wing is relayed through downwash recirculation into leading edge forward thrust. An airplane may glide with a nose-high attitude such that it might seem that forces on the wing would produce rearward acceleration. However, the force of leading edge suction, derived from downwash production, is sufficient to maintain forward movement. This is the mechanism of trading altitude and gravitational work for airspeed and glide distance.

In World War I, some bombers were equipped with cables strung in a sort of V shape from nose to wing tips for the purpose of deflecting barrage balloon tether cables. In pull out from dives it was noted that the airplane cables grew slack as the wings strained forward in production of forward thrust acting against fuselage drag.

By definition, lift is the aerodynamic force perpendicular to the flight path, while drag is defined as force parallel to the flight path. Thus it is lift which maintains the forward movement in the declined path of sinking flight. In this, forward thrust is derived in energy transfer from downwash to the leading edge.

Perpendicularity of lift to the wing flight path will be a factor in *adverse yaw* to be mentioned in a later section.

Stop Abusing Bernoulli! How Airplanes Really Fly

III. VISCOSITY

Viscosity Fundamentals

Air consists mostly of empty space. A volume of air at normal conditions is only about 0.1 percent occupied by molecules of nitrogen and oxygen plus other minor gases. The molecules are constantly in random motion of all directions with average speed, related to temperature, of about 1,500 feet per second, but the average molecule travels only about two millionths of an inch before colliding with another molecule. For air we regard as not being in motion, average molecular velocities are equal in all directions so that the average velocity of a volume of air in any direction is zero. Air we regard as being in motion, for example at ten miles per hour, would have overall average molecular *velocity* of about 15 feet per second in a specific direction, although average molecular random direction *speed* would remain in the neighborhood of 1,500 feet per second.

In a solid, molecules are anchored in an elastic manner, able to vibrate in any direction. Heat content determines the vibration amplitudes. The surface of the solid, even if highly polished, is still rough at the molecular level. Vibrating surface molecules interact with impacting air molecules. A surface molecule may absorb energy from an impacting air molecule, or it may bat an incoming air molecule away with increased departing energy. Coupling of random molecular motion between a solid surface and adjacent air is the mechanism of heat transfer.

If the adjacent air molecules have non-zero average velocity, then the air is considered to be flowing, and drag force results from intermolecular collisions between surface and air. The property of drag coupling between flow and a surface is known as *viscosity*. Viscous coupling also occurs between adjacent air masses of differing velocity as randomly moving molecules pass between the masses so that the velocities intermix. This coupling increases greatly if turbulence is present.

37

Coanda Effect, or Surface Attachment

Coanda discovered that flow would follow a surface, even when the surface curves away from flow, as illustrated in Figure 3.1. This phenomenon results from viscous and sometimes turbulent coupling between passing flow and relatively stagnant air nearer the surface. As near surface air is dragged rearward by viscous coupling of momentum from passing flow, and thereby removed, the vacated space it had occupied is refilled by passing flow, forced by pressure of surrounding atmosphere to curve with the surface. Coanda discovered flow attachment at age 21 while riding the cow-catcher of a steam railroad locomotive at night using lantern light for illumination of his experiments. Presumably Coanda did not encounter any cows, for he survived to later reach the position of Chief Engineer of Bristol Aircraft, a large British manufacturer of airplanes. The surface attachment phenomenon was named *Coanda effect* in his honor.

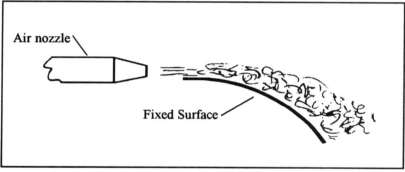

Figure 3.1 **Momentum Coupling in Coanda Effect**

As flow passes over a curved surface, stagnant air between flow and the surface is dragged away by viscous and perhaps turbulent coupling between flow and relatively stationary air. Atmospheric pressure then forces flow to curve so as to fill the space vacated by stagnant air removal.

The Boundary Layer

Viscous coupling from passing flow cannot remove all stagnant or slow moving air near a surface. Flow very near the surface loses essentially all of its ordered momentum and flow velocity through interaction with surface roughness. At increasing distance from the surface, interaction with the surface decreases, and velocity gradually increases toward becoming equal to the passing free stream. Thus a gradient is established where air velocity at the surface is essentially that of the surface, or zero, and becomes equal to the free stream at some distance out. The affected flow, known as the *boundary layer*, becomes deeper as flow proceeds aft, as illustrated in Figure 3.2.

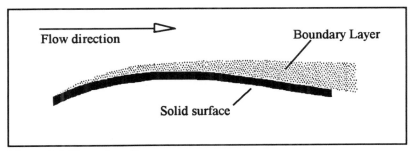

Figure 3.2 **Boundary Layer**

Viscous coupling between surface and passing flow produces a *boundary layer* of retarded flow which increases in depth rearward. Relative velocity is near zero at the surface, increasing toward that of undisturbed passing flow in the boundary layer outer portion.

Flow Separation

Pressure above the convex upper surface of a lifting wing or airfoil is reduced in the centrifugal gradient which partially offsets atmospheric pressure. Rearward-moving air approaching the low pressure region is subjected to the gradient of decreasing pressure, and is accelerated rearward into it. As the air accelerates rearward, work done on it by the pressure gradient causes flow to increase in kinetic energy content. Then, as flow passes on rearward from the minimum pressure region toward normal atmospheric pressure, kinetic energy is absorbed by pressure gradient opposition. In Bernoullian flow, without viscous drag, kinetic energy gained in pressure decrease would exactly equal that required to overcome the aft pressure increase. However, because some kinetic energy is lost in viscous drag, the boundary layer lacks required energy to complete its aft journey without assistance.

Opposition of the aft pressure gradient to boundary layer flow can cause a buildup of retarded air, as indicated in Figure 3.3, which may cause *flow separation* in which passing flow is diverted away from the surface.

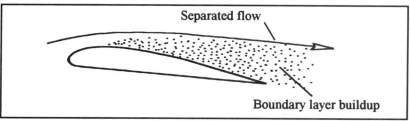

Figure 3.3 **Flow Separation**

Pressure gradient opposition to rearward flow causes diminished energy boundary layer flow to stagnate and build in depth. Buildup can become sufficient to significantly impair airfoil effectiveness.

Assistance for continued aft boundary layer flow is provided by rearward viscous drag from higher velocity adjacent flow. The assistance can be improved by introduction of a small degree of turbulence to intermix relatively unretarded adjacent flow with boundary layer flow so as to increase the coupling between them. On model airplanes, wing leading edges are sometimes roughened to provide the required turbulence.

Reynolds Number

On full sized airplanes, required turbulence occurs naturally at a position on the wing where the *laminar* (smooth) boundary layer has reached a depth such that it becomes unstable, causing localized separation, as indicated in Figure 3.4. Aft of this position the now turbulent but attached boundary layer continues aft. The localized separation is referred to as a *separation bubble*.

The tendency for boundary layer flow to become turbulent is related to factors of air density, velocity, length of path and viscosity. The interaction of these factors was established by British engineer and physicist Osborne Reynolds (1842-1912), while working with flows through pipes. His finding of the combined effect of the above factors was expressed as a simple ratio now known as the *Reynolds number*.

40

The Reynolds number is expressed as:

(3-1) $$Re = \rho v l / \mu$$

where ρ is density, v is velocity, l is length of path and μ is viscosity.

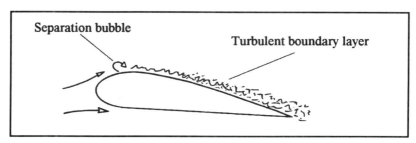

Figure 3.4 **Separation Bubble**

As the rearward-moving laminar boundary layer on the upper surface of an airplane wing becomes progressively thicker and less stable, shear forces tear it into a turbulent state in a *separation bubble* where a local flow reversal occurs. In this turbulence, adjacent higher velocity flow is mixed into the boundary layer which then continues aft as an attached turbulent layer.

Lift of a Paper in Coanda Effect

Viscosity is an important factor in a popular demonstration of aerodynamic lift operating on a sheet of paper, as indicated in Figure 3.5. When one blows air over the paper, viscous coupling and removal of stagnant air causes the flow stream to bend and follow the paper contour. Resulting lift of the paper is usually credited to "Bernoulli effect" or "Bernoulli principle." Lowered pressure is said to be caused by velocity of the air stream. However, this is not the true cause of lift, as can be shown in the similar experiment of Figure 3.6, where air is blown beneath the paper instead of above it.

In the first paper demonstration, lift is caused by upward centrifugal pressure acting against atmospheric pressure so as to produce pressure reduction at the paper upper surface. In the second demonstration,

41

upward centrifugal pressure is acting against the paper lower surface so as to add to atmospheric pressure, thus increasing pressure there. In both cases, lift is a result of downward acceleration of air mass and upward reaction force thereto. Clearly, viscosity is essential to lift in the first instance, but appears to have no role in the second. This raises a question of whether or not viscosity is necessary for wing operation.

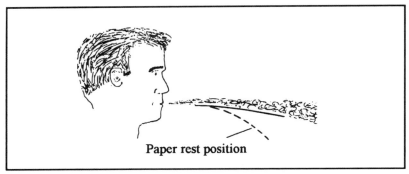

Figure 3.5 **Aerodynamic Lift Demonstration**

Flow attachment over a convex surface creates an outward centrifugal pressure gradient partially offsetting atmospheric pressure at the surface. If the surface is free to move it will tend to align with the initial direction of flow.

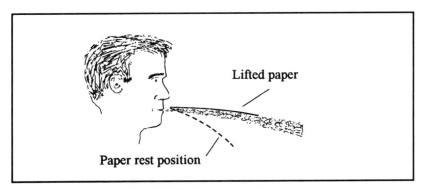

Figure 3.6 **Alternate Paper Lift Demonstration**

The pressure force is always away from the center of flow curvature. Below the flowing air, pressure is that of surrounding atmosphere, but force of the curving flow makes pressure at the paper lower surface greater. Thus lift is produced.

Classical induction theory maintains that viscosity is essential to lift. It is said to be necessary for creation of the starting vortex at a wing trailing edge so as to initiate the lift process. Without viscosity it is maintained that lift would not occur.

The induction theory concept of non-viscous air flow around an airfoil or wing is sometimes illustrated as in Figure 3.7. In flow around the "sharp trailing edge," the focus of pressure reduction in the centrifuging flow is on very small or infinitesimal area so that pressure becomes "negative," and velocity according to the Bernoulli theorem becomes very high or infinite around the edge. Flows would then merge aft with no net deflection and produce no lift or drag. Negative pressure is, of course, just a mathematical concept. In addition to being non-viscous, negative pressure would require the air to also have adhesive and cohesive properties.

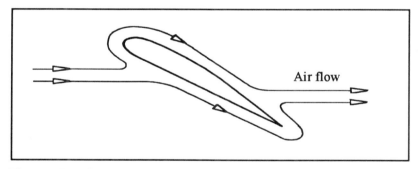

Figure 3.7 A Concept of Non-viscous Flow Passing an Airfoil

Conceptually, it is said non-viscous flow would divide between upper and lower flows which would re-converge aft with no directional change so that there would be no net lift or drag. However, since no non-viscous fluid exists, it is not possible to verify this concept.

A Simple Experiment

In some textbooks one can find illustrations of lift generated in passage of flow over a rotating cylinder. It is usually implied that viscous drag from the rotation is necessary for circulation and resulting lift to be generated. A simple and easy demonstration of rotating cylinder lift can be accomplished with a few commonly found household materials. Included are a ruler, about ten feet of thread, an 8 1/2 by 11 sheet of paper and some cellophane tape. The process is as follows:

Roll the paper into a cylinder of about 1 1/2 inches diameter with the longer dimension of the paper establishing the cylinder axial length. Tape the cylinder in a couple of places so that it will not unroll. Cut the thread into two equal pieces and tape one end of each thread to the cylinder near opposite ends. After laying the threads parallel on a flat surface, roll the cylinder along them so that the threads wind onto the cylinder. With the ruler parallel to the cylinder, tape the loose thread ends to the ruler. Now you are ready for the experiment.

Hold the cylinder and ruler horizontally at head height above the floor, and release the cylinder so that the threads unwind as the cylinder falls. As indicated in Figure 3.8, it will be seen that the cylinder does not fall vertically, but follows a curved path which indicates that lift is being developed in a direction perpendicular to the line of travel.

The classical explanation is that rotation of the cylinder induces circulation through viscous drag at its rotating surface, resulting in lift. The logical conclusion is that viscosity is necessary for lift, and without rotation to produce rotational viscous drag in the boundary layer a cylinder will not produce lift. In a later section we shall see that this is a mistaken belief. Non-rotating cylinders can and do produce lift and recirculation.

D'Alembert's Paradox

Jean Le Rond D'Alembert (1717-1783), named after Chapel St. Jean Lerond where he was abandoned on the steps as an infant, grew up to become a brilliant mathematician, philosopher and astronomer. He was interested in aerodynamics, and to develop understanding he considered theoretical performance of imaginary ideal air having no viscosity. He was surprised to conclude that without viscosity there would be no drag. This conclusion became known as D'Alembert's Paradox. However, it is

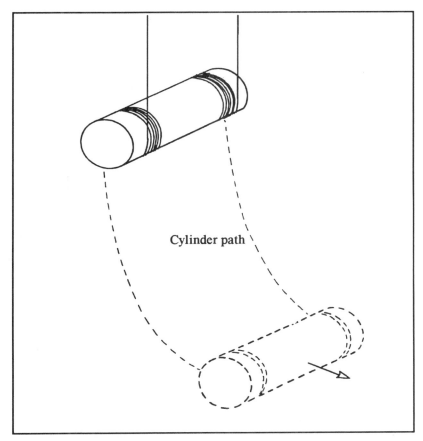

Figure 3.8 **Falling Cylinder**

As the paper cylinder falls with threads unwinding it follows a curved path which indicates that lift is being produced.

not difficult to imagine how non-viscous flow might produce no drag on a circular cylinder, as illustrated in Figure 3.9. D'Alembert's conclusion, that without viscosity there could be no aerodynamic drag is well accepted by the aerodynamics community, as is the conclusion that without viscosity there can be no lift.

In the earlier description of Coanda effect, viscosity was described as the source of drag for carrying away stagnant air from near a surface so that flow attachment occurs. This would be true in the case of a non-accelerating surface in accelerating flow, as in Figure 3.1. However, in the

45

case of an airplane wing accelerating into forward movement from being stopped, mass inertia of air would tend to make it stay behind. Thus stagnant air buildup could only accumulate as a result of viscous drag. From this we must conclude that viscosity is both source and solution of a potential problem.

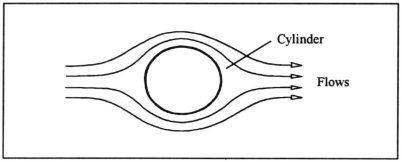

Figure 3.9 **Cylinder in Non-Viscous Flow**

Non-viscous flow impacting on the leading edge of a cylinder would produce a forward region of pressure rise from which rearward flows would centrifuge outward, producing equally reduced pressure regions at upper and lower surfaces. From the front, air would accelerate rearward into the mid-surface lowest pressure regions and would decelerate from there on rearward. Convergence of upper and lower flows aft of the cylinder would cause another pressure rise at the rear equal to that at the front, producing rearward acceleration of parting flow to its original velocity. Overall, vertical and fore-aft thrust forces would be in opposing balance so that there would be no net lift or drag.

If viscosity is indeed necessary for lift generation, then we must embrace it as essential to flight, even though it produces undesirable drag effects. However, this is only a theoretical concept of academic value, and cannot be verified by experiment, since there is no non-viscous fluid.

Could the belief that viscosity is necessary for lift be wrong? It is clear that the sharp trailing edge is not really necessary. A flat board with rounded edges in real air will produce lift, but would it not produce lift if air were non-viscous?

Wind Gradient

In addition to aerodynamics of the airplane, we must also deal with aerodynamics of the natural environment in which we fly. Of the environmental factors, wind gradient is perhaps the least recognized and most poorly presented in existing publications for pilots. FAA publications, for example, usually deal with wind as just a matter of difference between air speed and ground speed, and overlook the more subtle but quite important effects of wind gradient on airplane performance during takeoff and landing. Figure 3.10 illustrates the effect of wind on climb performance as most often described.

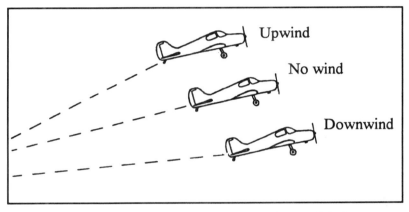

Figure 3.10 **Popular Concept of the Effect of Wind on Climbout**

If wind were of constant speed without regard to distance from the surface, the effect of wind on climb after takeoff would be only on groundspeed. Upwind and downwind takeoffs would differ only in length of ground run and in ground speed at lift-off. There would be no difference in rate of climb or pitch attitude for holding constant airspeed.

Wind gradient near ground level, like a boundary layer, is caused by surface resistance to air flow. Surface drag produces near-surface turbulence and a gradient of velocity. Turbulence and gradient depth are affected by trees, buildings and other objects. Because of the gradient, the effects of wind on takeoff and landing performance are more subtle and yet more profound than most publications indicate. Figure 3.11 better illustrates the true effect including that of gradient. The difference in pitch attitude for holding constant airspeed during climb can be impressive if the wind is strong. Significant wind gradients may exist to altitudes of two hundred to over one-thousand feet.

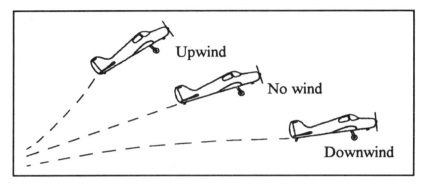

Figure 3.11 **True Effect of Wind Gradient on Climbout**

As an airplane climbs into a gradient of increasing headwind, the increasing wind adds to airspeed. If constant airspeed is held by pitch attitude, then ground speed continuously decreases and the climb rate is made greater as kinetic energy of the slowing airplane is converted to potential energy associated with altitude. In downwind takeoff the result is opposite. The increasing tailwind during climb subtracts from airspeed, and pitch attitude may have to be lowered to avoid stall.

During a windy, sunny day, thermal stirring from surface heating energizes near-surface wind just as separation bubble turbulence energizes a wing boundary layer. Then at night, surface cooling by radiation into a clear night sky produces a cool blanket of relatively stagnant surface air, and a strong wind gradient at the top of the cool layer. In downwind takeoff into the apparent calm, the effect of encountering the tail wind gradient is much like partially losing engine power. Climb rate can decrease dramatically, and clearance of obstructions may become cause for concern.

The Downwind Turn Controversy

In early days of powered flight a fear of "downwind turns" developed. Many have claimed that fear of the downwind turn is without any reasonable basis. The reasoning is that an airplane flies in the air environment alone and is not affected by the relation of air movement with respect to the ground. This seems reasonable if one does not consider the effects of wind gradient.

In climbing out of takeoff in a headwind with a strong wind gradient the angle of ascent may safely be made unusually steep. Then if a turn to crosswind is made, the increasing headwind in climb ceases, and the climb attitude may have to be reduced to prevent stall.

A more important consideration however, is that in a turn one wingtip is higher than the other. Suppose a low altitude turn left turn from upwind to crosswind is made in a strong gradient, as indicated in Figure 3.12.

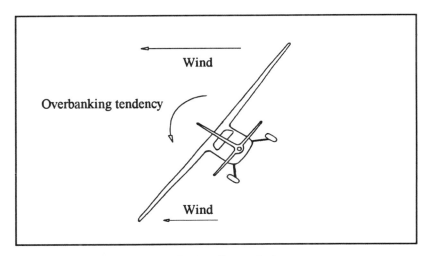

Figure 3.12 **Turn From Upwind to Crosswind**

In a low altitude turn from upwind in a strong wind gradient, a tendency to overbank begins when the bank is initiated, due to greater airspeed at the higher wing. The situation worsens as the turn approaches crosswind, as indicated above, where the wind gradient makes the angle of attack of the higher wing greater than that of the lower.

In a steep left turn the right wingtip of a typical lightplane may be more than 25 feet higher than the left where the difference in wind speed will tend to roll the plane into a greater bank. If the pilot is hesitant or timid about applying hard right aileron to counter the roll, or if aileron effectiveness of the plane is not sufficient, the roll may continue to an inverted condition followed by a dive to the ground. Students are often taught to make no turns below 400 feet. This greatly reduces the potential for such accidents.

Stop Abusing Bernoulli!
How Airplanes Really Fly

IV. STALL

Rapid Increase of Lift Coefficient

In Figure 2.8 we saw plots of lift versus angle of attack. In such plots it is not customary to include information as to the rate of change of angle of attack during data gathering. As long as the rate of change corresponds with what is normal in airplane flight through still air, it may be considered unimportant. However, helicopter rotor airfoils are tested at rapid rates of pitch change related to those of rotor application wherein the angle of attack is cycled rapidly to maintain some degree of uniformity of lift through each rotation. Figure 4.1 illustrates lift versus angle of attack of an airfoil section during testing with a rapid rate of pitch increase, and with a slow rate of increase.

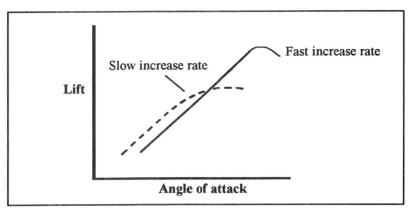

Figure 4.1 **Effect of Rate of Increase of Angle of Attack on Peak Lift**

The dashed line above indicates lift versus angle of attack for a helicopter airfoil section during slow rate of increase of angle of attack. The solid line indicates lift at a fast rate of increase. Note that the fast rate of lift increase produces peak lift nearly one and one-half times that of slow increase, after which lift falls quite rapidly.

The phenomenon of decline of lift at greater angles of attack is caused by boundary layer buildup and flow separation, and is known as *stall*. We normally think of stall as bad, because nasty things can result for the unwary pilot. However, stall serves a valuable function of limiting stresses on the aircraft structure. From the above illustration we can see that a fast increase can result in considerably greater stress. Because of this, pilots are taught to slow to *maneuvering speed* in heavy turbulence in order to avoid excessive stresses which can result if a momentary downdraft, which reduces the effective angle of attack, is followed by sudden updraft which quickly increases the angle of attack.

In the case of fast increase of angle of attack, rapid rise of lift is followed by very abrupt decline as stall occurs. It is important to understand what is involved in this lift and stall, for it relates to several aspects of wing design. To begin this understanding, let us first consider the aerodynamic behavior of a circular cylinder in flow perpendicular to the cylinder axis.

Cylinder Aerodynamics

In many books one can find illustrations and photographs of flows past circular cylinders. It is commonly known that flow past a cylinder can produce downstream eddies of alternating rotational direction. These eddies have become known as *Karman vortices,* and the trail of them has become known as the *Karman vortex street.* Most text books treat the vortices as little more than curiosities, and provide little explanation. However, this process of alternating vortices production involves continuous cycles of lift generation, with periodic stall and lift reversals which deflect downstream yarn tufts in alternating direction, as shown in Figure 4.2. We shall cover this process in detail because it relates intimately to the airplane wing stall process and wing design.

It is common knowledge that rotation of a cylinder can produce sustained lift and flow deflection in a direction corresponding to that of rotation. This is shown in Figure 4.3, where the cylinder is being rotated in a clockwise direction. Viscous drag and boundary layer buildup in downward flow on the left side are increased by upward surface movement.

Oppositely, right side stall is prevented by surface movement which carries the boundary layer downward. Thus clockwise circulation and cylinder lift to the right, with accompanying flow deflection to the left, is favored by clockwise rotation.

Figure 4.2 **Cylinder in Downflow**

The cylinder above has narrow surface slots through which boundary layer air can be withdrawn into a rotatable central tube mount. The stationary black strip indicates that the cylinder is not rotating. Also no boundary layer air is being withdrawn. Alternating lift with left and right flow deflections causes the yarn tufts to be deflected left and right, producing blurred fan-like images.

Figure 4.3 **Cylinder with Clockwise Rotation**

With clockwise rotation, downward surface movement on the right side carries the boundary layer through the aft pressure gradient. Lift toward the right is sustained without stall, and tuft deflection is sustained toward the left.

53

In Figure 4.4, opposite direction of rotation produces opposite boundary layer effects so that resultant lift and tuft deflection are reversed.

Figure 4.4 Cylinder with Counter-clockwise Rotation

With counter-clockwise rotation, stall is prevented with lift toward the left, and tuft deflection is sustained toward the right.

In the two preceding photographs no boundary layer removal is being exercised. Compare these with the next two photos, Figures 4.5 and 4.6, which are in conditions of no rotation but with boundary layer removal by internal suction. Again stall does not occur, and lift can be sustained in either direction.

Figure 4.5 Cylinder With Boundary Layer Removal

Without rotation, but with boundary layer suction removal through narrow surface slots, stable lift develops spontaneously. In the above photo, lift is toward the right with tuft deflection to the left.

Figure 4.6 **Lift Reversal**

From conditions of the preceding photo, the direction of lift has been tripped into reversal by momentarily inserting an object near the cylinder to disturb the flow.

Although lift is sustained with either rotation or internal suction removal of the boundary layer, a degree of oscillation is still present, as indicated by small oscillations of the yarn tufts. This is because the angle of downwash is not precisely defined by a sharp trailing edge as in the case of an airfoil. Similar oscillation can occur when an airplane wing approaches stall with substantial flow separation. Separated flow does not closely follow the wing surface, and thus does not have well controlled direction. When this occurs, the resulting lift oscillations, commonly referred to as *buffeting,* can be felt by passengers.

As in the case of a cylinder without rotation or boundary layer removal, a non-rotating cylinder with boundary layer removal develops lift spontaneously, but differs in that lift is sustained in one direction. Lift may be initiated by any small flow unbalance or disturbance which quickly is amplified by the system until a limiting condition occurs. We may regard the process as regenerative in the sense that the starting of lift causes more lift to be generated.

At low Reynolds numbers, and without rotation, flow deflection is resisted by viscous forces, as illustrated in Figure 4.7, so that lift does not develop. Any tendency to produce flow deflection, recirculation and lift results in increased viscous drag where the aft flow path is longer and faster, and reduced drag where the path is shorter and slower. Thus at low Reynolds numbers the process can be regarded as *degenerative*.

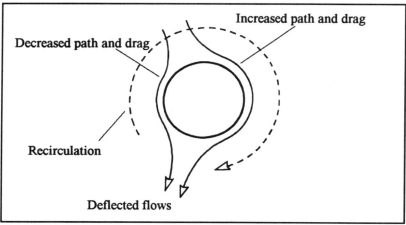

Figure 4.7 **Degenerative Viscous Drag**

When flow is laminar at low Reynolds number, any tendency for flow deflection to develop would be resisted by resulting viscous drag differential. On the lower pressure side where velocity and path length are increased, drag is increased. On the opposite side drag is decreased. The drag differential is sufficient to prevent flow deflection and enforce a stable condition of no lift

Regenerative and degenerative processes of the world may be electrical, mechanical, biological, or even social in nature. In general, regenerative processes increase to a limiting level where stabilization or reversal and oscillation may occur. Degenerative processes resist change and thus are inherently stable.

With increasing Reynolds number, flow separation can develop, as in Figure 4.8 where flows diverted away from the surface are less influenced by the stabilizing degenerative effect of viscous drag. With further increases, the regenerative influence of recirculation in boundary layer flow reinforcement becomes a more significant factor.

Momentum coupled from passing flow assists boundary layers down-ward movements on opposite sides of the cylinder. Effectiveness of this coupling is related to flow velocities adjacent to the boundary layers.

Any beginning of flow deflection and recirculation near the cylinder adds to flow velocity on one side and detracts from velocity on the other, with the result that boundary layer flow reinforcement is increased on the faster side and decreased on the other. The difference in reinforcement is in a direction to regeneratively promote further growth of flow deflection and recirculation.

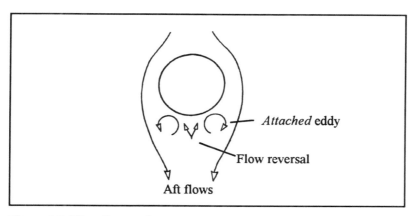

Figure 4.8 **Flow Separation**

As Reynolds number increases from the preceding illustration, the combination of increased aft pressure gradient and increased viscous drag reduces boundary layer energy to the point that outer flows converging aft of the cylinder produce pressure rise greater than that at the rear surface. Flow reversal then develops to produce the twin eddies shown, which are held as *attached* to the cylinder rear by the aft pressure gradient. With this flow separation the stabilizing effect of viscous surface drag is reduced.

At lower Reynolds numbers the predominant stability factor is viscous drag at the surface, but at higher Reynolds numbers the regenerative effect of recirculation reinforcement of the boundary layer dominates. In this condition flow deflection and recirculation rapidly grow, as indicated in Figure 4.9, toward a physical limit.

When lift reaches a maximum level, as indicated in Figure 4.10, the smaller eddy, which has been reduced by boundary layer reinforcement from recirculation, ceases to exist, and the opposite eddy has grown to maximum size.

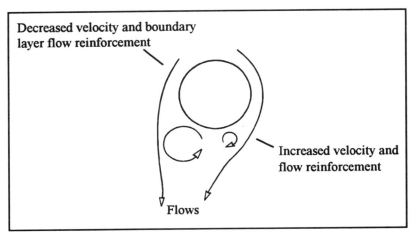

Figure 4.9 **Regenerative Effect of Clockwise Recirculation**

Any degree of flows unbalance or disturbance which initiates recirculation immediately affects the reinforcement of aft boundary layers flow in a differential manner so as to promote further unbalance and recirculation. As indicated above, clockwise circulation adds to velocity and boundary layer flow reinforcement on the right side while decreasing velocity and boundary flow reinforcement on the left. The difference in reinforcement promotes more clockwise recirculation.

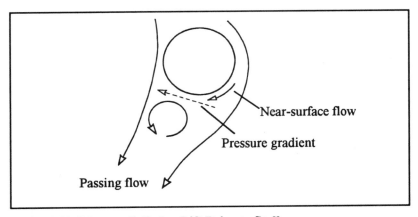

Figure 4.10 **Mature Cylinder Lift Prior to Stall**

When the cylinder has reached its peak of mature lift, the eddy on the side where recirculation provides greater boundary layer flow reinforcement has disappeared. The other eddy is fully grown. Continued near-surface flow between eddy and cylinder rear is opposed by the gradient of higher pressure on the left side and lower on the right.

58

At maturity, a balance exists at the cylinder rear between pressure gradient and kinetic energy of near-surface flow. With further lift increase, the aft pressure gradient is greater, and boundary layer flow again begins to accumulate on the lower pressure side. The accumulation quickly affects lift, recirculation and boundary layer reinforcement so that stall occurs quite rapidly.

In stall, the residual pressure gradient initiates a reversal of aft flow deflection, as shown in Figure 4.11, which in turn initiates reversal and a new regenerative buildup of lift in the opposite direction. This buildup rapidly grows until stall again occurs, followed by another reversal. The process continues as a series of oscillating lift reversals.

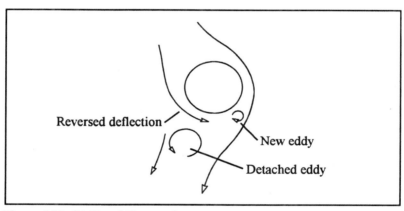

Figure 4.11 **Stall and Reversal**

With a pressure gradient at the cylinder rear greater than energy of flow from the right surface can overcome, a new flow separation, represented in the smaller eddy above, is initiated. The centrifugal gradient aft of the cylinder initiates a reversal of aft flow deflection, and a consequent reversal of recirculation and direction of lift. The mature eddy is detached in the reversal and carried downstream.

In each reversal, circulation growth is accompanied by growth of an aft vortex of equal but opposite angular momentum. Unlike the cylinder, an airfoil limits the downwash angle to the direction pointed by the trailing edge. Thus in normal flight the stall condition is not reached, and reversal of lift does not occur. However, with operation at a high lift coefficient, an attached vortex may occur near the trailing edge as in Figure 4.12.

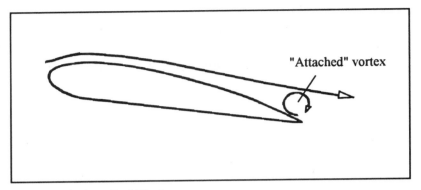

Figure 4.12 **Attached Vortex**

In operation at high lift coefficient, an *attached* vortex, analogous to the new eddy of Figure 4.11, may appear near an airfoil trailing edge. If the lift coefficient is further increased, stall can occur, but the downward-pointing trailing edge will not permit upward flow deflection and reversed lift.

As lift is generated, downwash recirculation initiated around the airfoil grows outwardly, as indicated in Figure 4.13. All recirculation contributes to lift, but only new recirculation near the surface can couple energy into the upper surface boundary layer. If initial near-surface recirculation is intense because of a suddenly steep downwash angle, then upper surface boundary layer flow reinforcement is especially effective. Thus with a rapidly increasing angle of attack, as in the case of the helicopter airfoil test, intense near-surface recirculation produces a high degree of boundary layer energization so that lift can reach an unsustainably high transient level.

Insects make use of transient high coefficient lift with wings too small for sustained non-cycling flight. Insect flight is not well understood, but future understanding might possibly lead to some interesting very small scale applications in the moving of air or other gases, in scientific instruments, for example.

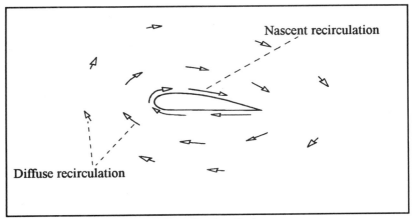

Figure 4.13 **Nascent and Diffuse Recirculation**

Downwash left behind the forward moving airfoil is forced to recirculate around newer more intense recirculation nearer the airfoil. Only the new recirculation, which we may refer to as nascent, can add energy to the boundary layer. Farther out recirculation, which we may refer to as diffuse, carries most of the energy and momentum , and produces most of the lift.

Stop Abusing Bernoulli!
How Airplanes Really Fly

V. AIRFOIL BASICS

Evolution

In early years of heavier-than-air flight, wings were made as thin as possible because drag was regarded as mainly a function of frontal area impacted by passing flow. Sir George Cayley's "Boy Glider," of 1849, the first successful glider to carry a human occupant in flight (for a few yards) was a triplane (having three sets of wings) with thin flat fabric wings of low aspect ratio. As further efforts at manned flight were made it was learned that wings were more effective if they were curved, or cambered, as illustrated below.

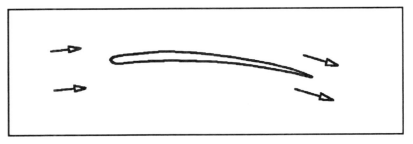

Figure 5.1 **Early Cambered Airfoil**

Curvature of a thin wing or airfoil profile, better accommodating flow curvature from upwash to downwash was found to improve the lift to drag ratio. The Wright brothers used wings of similar shape.

Early thin wings usually consisted of wooden frameworks covered with coated fabric. To obtain strength and rigidity, and to maintain aerodynamic properties while supporting an airframe, an engine and a pilot, they evolved into biplane structure with upper and lower wings having multiple struts and wires between for bracing, as in Figure 5.2.

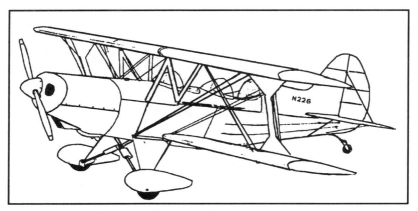

Figure 5.2 **Biplane Structure**

Biplanes achieve strength through inter-wing bracing. This was an important advantage in early airplanes which had flimsy thin wings.

In World War I it was recognized by Ludwig Prandtl that thickness was not only acceptable, but quite desirable. The German Dr-1 triplane, designed by Fokker who was Dutch, was first to have a thick airfoil. The thicker airfoil was found to be more effective over a wide range of operating conditions. With it, the Dr-1 was more maneuverable than any fighter of the allies, and had a better climb rate. Later Fokker biplanes were even better.

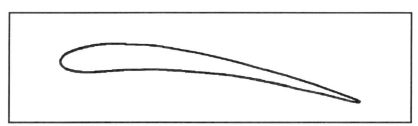

Figure 5.3 **Thicker Leading Edge**

German Fokkers were first to use a thicker leading edge wing. This greatly improved maneuverability and low speed operation in climb. The famous German Red Baron flew a Fokker triplane with the thicker wings.

With a thicker frontal region, a wing can have a more broadly rounded leading edge so that it can accommodate a greater range of upwash angles associated with varying loading and airspeed conditions. Thickness also provides for greater rigidity and strength. Upon learning of the thicker airfoil and its advantages, the British were hesitant to use it because it was covered by Fokker's Dutch patent. The Dutch were neutral in the war.

Later it was learned that concave curvature of a wing lower surface was of little aerodynamic importance. Wings were then made even thicker with much greater strength, as indicated in Figure 5.4.

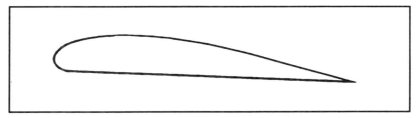

Figure 5.4 **Typical More Modern Wing Contour**

Wings have evolved from the early thin designs having concave lower surfaces. Modern design is characterized by a more rounded leading edge to better accommodate varying upwash entry angles, a convex upper surface tailored for minimization of adverse boundary layer effects while guiding upper surface flow from upwash to downwash, and a sharp trailing edge for smooth mergence of upper and lower surface flows.

With thicker, more rigid wings the biplane structure became no longer necessary. The greater thickness also allowed for in-wing fuel tanks so that more cabin space became available. Airplanes then evolved into predominately *monoplane*, single wing designs.

Some experimental planes, the X-15 rocket plane for example, were built with blunt trailing edges. At high supersonic speeds, a sharp trailing edge was of no value, for flows would not have smoothly merged at the rear, and in low speed descent to landing, blunt trailing edge drag was desirable for slowing the airplane.

Camber

When operating normally in stable flight, the leading edge of a wing intercepts upwash flow which is redirected rearward and then downward as downwash at the trailing edge. For best efficiency in normal operation the airfoil is cambered to accommodate the curvature of flow. There is no ideal degree of camber for the full range of operation of a typical airplane wing. At low speed and heavy loading, when circulation is intense, a high degree of camber is needed, but at high speed when loading is light, a high degree of camber does not match the lesser curvature of circulation, and the excess camber contributes to *parasitic drag*. This can be seen in comparing the curves of Figure 5.5.

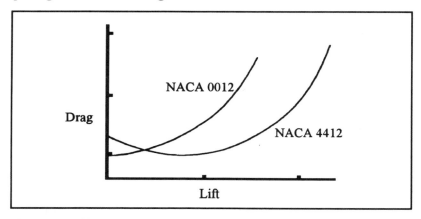

Figure 5.5 **Lift vs Drag of Cambered and Uncambered Airfoils**

Drag of the NACA 0012 uncambered airfoil is least at zero lift and increases with increasing lift. Drag of the NACA 4412 cambered, but otherwise similar airfoil, is higher at zero lift but decreases up to a point as lift increases. Its greater drag at lower lift is due to mismatch between curvature of the airfoil and little curvature of flow from upwash to downwash. At greater lifts and flow curvature, drag is less on the cambered NACA 4412.

The basic modern airfoil shape includes a rounded leading edge to accommodate differing upwash angles, camber to match flow curvature from upwash to downwash, and a thin trailing edge for smooth mergence of departing flows. In addition, surface curvatures need to be designed for minimum flow separation under influence of aft pressure gradient and viscosity effects.

Performance Coefficients

Lift was expressed earlier as equal to the product, $\pi \rho v^2 A \sin(\alpha - \alpha_0)$, where ρ is air density, v is airspeed, A is airfoil area, α is angle of attack and α_0 is angle of attack at zero lift. If we divide by area, A, we get *lift per unit area*, L', as:

(5-1)
$$L' = \pi \rho v^2 \sin(\alpha - \alpha_0)$$

This can be rewritten in a bit more complex manner as:

(5-2)
$$L' = \left(\frac{\rho v^2}{2}\right) [2\pi \sin(\alpha - \alpha_0)]$$

where the quantity in brackets, $[2\pi \sin(\alpha - \alpha_0)]$, is defined to be the theoretical *lift coefficient*. Here the angle, $(\alpha - \alpha_0)$, is the theoretical trailing edge downwash angle, sometimes referred to as absolute angle of attack. The expression applies to both cambered and uncambered airfoils, as illustrated in the following plot:

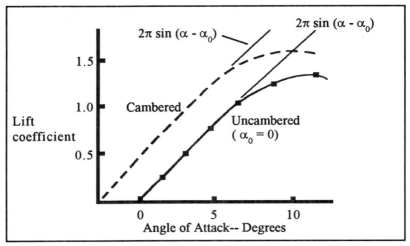

Figure 5.6 **Lift Coefficients vs Angle of Attack**

Lift coefficients for both cambered and uncambered airfoils tend to track the $2\pi \sin(\alpha - \alpha_0)$ lines, but for the uncambered airfoil, $\alpha_0 = 0$. For the cambered airfoil line above, α_0 is approximately minus three degrees.

67

The variables of air density, ρ, and airspeed, v, are factors of the flight environment, which may be inserted into calculations of a potential user. Thus the custom of separating them out of performance data to obtain performance coefficient is understandable, but inclusion of multiplication by two, requiring division by two of the (ρv^2) product, with no net effect, is more mysterious. Apparently this is to relate forces to the Bernoulli theorem, in which pressure change is proportional to the product $(\rho v^2/2)$.

The *drag coefficient* is defined in a manner similar to that of the lift coefficient. Drag test data is divided by test section area and $(\rho v^2/2)$ before recording as drag coefficient.

Pitching Moment and Aerodynamic Center

The lift of an uncambered airfoil is centered about a position one-quarter chord aft of the leading edge throughout the normal operating range. If we were to mount an uncambered airfoil section so as to be pivotable about an axis located along the quarter-chord center of lift, no torque would be required to maintain the desired angle of attack over the normal operating range. If the axis of pivot were offset ahead of or behind this center of lift location the lift force would produce a torque, known as *pitching moment*, about that axis.

A cambered airfoil has no location about which pitching moment would remain zero over a range of angles of attack. However, it does have a location, known as the *aerodynamic center*, about which the pitching moment remains relatively constant through normal angle of attack operating range. At zero lift angle of attack, where the departing downwash angle is zero, a cambered airfoil produces a pitching moment which is unaffected by selection of axis location. Like other airfoil forces, pitching moment is a Newtonian force due to accelerations of air mass. As illustrated in Figure 5.7, upward acceleration of air mass at the front portion of the non-lifting cambered airfoil produces downward reaction force, and as flow passes on toward the rear, the upward air mass movement is intercepted to produce an upward force on the aft portion of the airfoil. These opposite forces constitute the pitching moment.

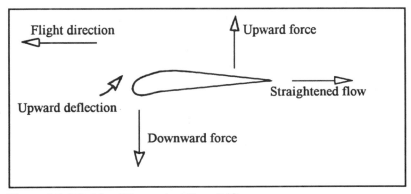

Figure 5.7 **Pitching Moment at Zero Lift**

Upward deflection of flow in the forward portion of the airfoil produces a downward reaction force there. As flow passes on, the upward movement is intercepted as flow is redirected rearward. In interception of the upward movement an upward force is produced in reaction. Together the upward and downward forces constitute a negative *pitching moment* which tends to pitch the airfoil to a lesser, or more negative, angle of attack.

Torque produced by a force couple is proportional to the distance between the forces. Thus pitching moment is related to airfoil chord length. Lift, drag and pitching forces are represented as:

$$(5\text{-}3) \qquad \text{Lift} = (\frac{\rho v^2}{2})AC_L$$

$$(5\text{-}4) \qquad \text{Drag} = (\frac{\rho v^2}{2})AC_D$$

$$(5\text{-}5) \qquad \text{Moment} = (\frac{\rho v^2}{2})ACC_M$$

In the above, A is airfoil area, C_L is lift coefficient, C_D is drag coefficient, C_M is moment coefficient, and C is airfoil chord. Note that chord is an explicit factor of multiplication in pitching moment because of its effect on distance between upward and downward thrust centers.

69

Pitching moment is usually regarded as being a property of cambered airfoils or wings only. However, regardless of whether or not an airfoil has camber, pitching moment is a matter of where the lift and drag forces exist in relation to the location about which pivoting forces are evaluated. Consider Figure 5.8 which illustrates forces about a position near mid-chord of a uniformly curved airfoil section somewhat similar to a design of the Wright brothers. In a wind tunnel which allows no lateral losses, upwash interception lift at zero angle of attack equals that of downwash production, and lift is centered near the mid-chord position.

With lift force centered on the pivot of Figure 5.8a, there is no resulting moment about the center. When the angle of attack is gradually changed to that producing no downwash, and hence zero lift, as in Figure 5.8b, then a pitching moment is created which is due entirely to camber.

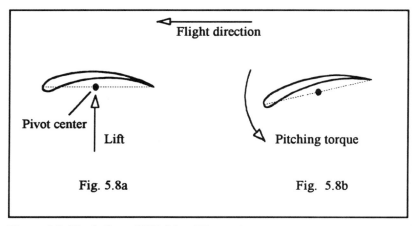

Figure 5.8 **Variation of Pitching Moment**

In the left illustration, where lift is centered near mid-chord, no torque exists around the mid-chord pivot point, but when the angle of attack is changed to that of zero lift, a pitching moment is created because of camber.

Now let us consider pitching moment variation about a carefully chosen pivot center near the quarter-chord position, as shown in Figure 5.9. The moment due to lift in Figure 5.9a is equal to the moment due to camber at zero lift in Figure 5.9b. About this position, known as the aerodynamic center, pitching moment is essentially independent of angle of attack.

70

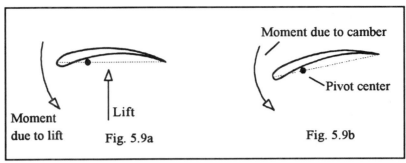

Figure 5.9 **Aerodynamic Center**

In the left illustration, lift centered at mid-chord produces torque about the pivot located near the quarter-chord position. In the right illustration there is no lift, but torque due to camber is equal to that produced by lift in the left illustration. As the angle of attack varies between these positions, the torque, or moment, remains nearly constant. This position, which may or may not be on the chord line, is known as the *aerodynamic center.*

Center of Pressure

The center of pressure is usually defined as a location on the chord line, or extension of it, where the combined forces of lift, drag and moment can be resolved as a single linear force, as illustrated in Figure 5.10.

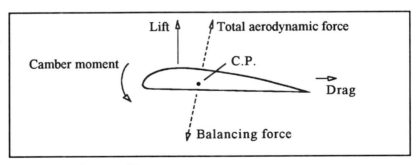

Figure 5.10 **Center of Pressure**

Lift and drag act about some axis where they combine to produce a positive moment, or clockwise torque, which precisely balances the negative moment or counter-clockwise torque due to camber. At this location all wing aerodynamic forces can be balanced by a single linear force. This location, known as the center of pressure, varies as a function of lift coefficient. The balancing force combines airplane weight, engine thrust, fuselage drag etc.

For a symmetric or uncambered airfoil, the center of pressure is located one-quarter chord aft of the leading edge throughout the normal operating range. Thus around this position the pitching moment remains zero and hence, since it is constant at this position, this is also the aerodynamic center.

The center of pressure of a cambered airfoil varies in position from far aft at low lift coefficient to near the quarter-chord point at high lift coefficient. This is near the aerodynamic center, but normally slightly aft in order that the negative pitching moment remain.

Starting and Bound Vortices Balance

Even at zero lift, drag and pitching moment can be resolved into a single linear force. In this case the point of resolution would be external to the airfoil. Transmission of angular momentum requires a minimum of two non co-linear forces forming a couple. Because the forces of lift, drag and pitching moment are resolvable into a single linear force, it follows that no net angular momentum is transmitted from the airfoil to the air. Thus angular momentum of circulation must be equaled by opposite-direction angular momentum of the vortex left behind.

In induction theory, an equivalent condition, taken from vortex theory, is that no net vorticity can be produced. This is the basis of the assumption that the starting vortex causes equal circulation vorticity of opposite direction around the wing in order to maintain zero net change. The concept of equal and opposite vortices is without fault, but the assumed cause and effect relationship is without justification. The real cause is downward air displacement in downwash, and the effect is upward recirculation in equal and opposite patterns of the "starting vortex" and "circulation" around the wing.

Stop Abusing Bernoulli!
How Airplanes Really Fly

VI. RECIRCULATION IN THREE DIMENSIONS

"Induced" Drag vs Span

Thus far we have been considering uniform rectangular airfoil sections spanning wall-to-wall in a wind tunnel where no lateral air movement was produced. This restriction permitted development of a lift equation and a basic concept of airfoil action. Now we shall consider unconfined applications of airfoils as wings and control surfaces of airplanes, where downwash recirculation is partially lost laterally into trailing vortices, as was indicated in Figure 2.5. Continuous loss of energy into trailing vortices is a source of drag, which, in induction theory, is attributed to electromagnetic-like induction effects and is termed *induced drag*.

The portion of downwash which diverts into lateral recirculation is lost and unavailable for forward recycling into interceptable upwash. This partial loss of upwash interception results in partial loss of leading edge forward thrust and upward lift so that more engine thrust is required for flight.

Lateral recirculation of a wing operating in unconfined airspace is produced from the same pressure forces which produce recoverable bound recirculation. Thus lateral recirculation intensity is proportional to that of bound recirculation. Since Γ represents velocity content, and kinetic energy varies with velocity squared, the trailing vortices kinetic energy loss rate is proportional to Γ squared. This means that vortices drag, or "induced drag" loss is proportional to Γ squared, assuming other factors to be constant, or:

$$(6\text{-}1) \qquad\qquad D_i \propto \Gamma^2$$

From the Kutta-Joukowski theorem, lift $= \rho vS\Gamma$. If we maintain constant lift while varying the span, then Γ is inversely proportional to span, S, or:

(6-2) $$\Gamma \propto \frac{1}{S}$$

and drag due to vortices loss then becomes:

(6-3) $$D_i \propto \frac{1}{S^2}$$

Thus "induced" drag is inversely proportional to span squared. As an example of what this means, if an airplane wingspan of 28 feet were increased to 32 feet, with all other conditions, including weight, unchanged, induced drag would be reduced by a ratio of 28 squared to 32 squared, or about one-fourth.

Stall speed, important in takeoffs and landings, is a function of maximum lift coefficient and wing area. Area, for a rectangular wing, is the product of span and chord. The span to chord ratio is known as *aspect ratio*. As indicated in Figure 6.1, maximum lift coefficient is affected only slightly by aspect ratio. Thus stall speed is affected only slightly by aspect ratio, but the effect on vortices loss drag is quite significant. If required wing area is determined so as to establish approximate stall speed, then vortices loss drag, which is a function of span, becomes a function of aspect ratio. The effect of aspect ratio on drag can be seen in Figure 6.2, which relates lift to drag coefficients of differing aspect ratios of cambered wings.

In the curves of Figure 6.2, aspect ratio difference of the cambered wing exhibits little effect at low lift coefficients. This is because the wing, at very low lift coefficient, has excessive curvature in relation to the shallow angles of upwash and downwash. The camber mismatch results in such parasitic drag at low lift coefficients that induced drag and aspect ratio are of little importance. This would not be desirable as a normal condition, but could occur at higher airspeeds, perhaps with light loading and in cold dense air. The need for camber is greatest when operating at high lift coefficients, as during takeoff, landing and climb, when airspeed is low, and in high altitude high temperature operation with low air density, but camber can become a cause for inefficiency at low lift coefficients. As with other matters, good engineering demands compromises.

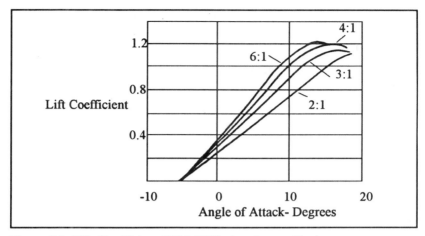

Figure 6.1 **Lift Coefficient With Differing Aspect Ratios**

Due to greater energy loss rate into trailing vortices, lift coefficients versus
angles of attack are lower with lower aspect ratios. However, the lower aspect
ratios are operable to higher angles of attack, and hence the maximum lift
coefficients of lower aspect ratio airfoils are nearly equal to those of higher
ratios.

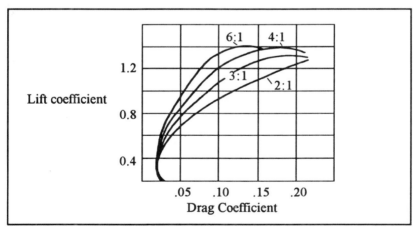

Figure 6.2 **Lift/Drag With Differing Aspect Ratios of a Cambered Wing**

The slope of lift coefficient versus drag coefficient increases with increasing
aspect ratio, because of lower energy loss rate into trailing vortices. This plot
includes both induced and parasitic drags.

At higher, increasing angles of attack, drag coefficients continue to increase even as lift coefficients peak and begin to decrease. Beyond peak lift, drag increases rapidly due to flow detachment and resulting parasitic losses. In the operating range of lift coefficients from about 0.8 to 1.2, curvatures of the plots indicate that drag increases proportionately faster than lift as coefficients are increased. This is because lift increases as a nearly linear function of trailing edge downwash velocity and resultant Γ while drag due to trailing vortices losses increases faster, in relation to Γ squared.

In most applications, higher lift coefficients are made possible for landing and takeoff by mechanically modifying wing characteristics for reduced speed. Stall speed, or minimum flight speed, can be obtained by rearranging equation (5-3) to yield the following :

$$(6\text{-}4) \qquad V_{stall} = \sqrt{\frac{2L}{\rho A C_{L\,max}}}$$

In the foregoing expression, L is lift force, or aircraft weight, ρ is air density, A is wing area, and C_{Lmax} is the maximum lift coefficient, where the lift curve peaks.

It is worth noting here that stall may have a different meaning for an airplane pilot. An airplane wing reaching the peak of the lift curve when lift coefficient is increasing due to airspeed decrease, angle of attack increase, or increase in loading due to maneuvering, is likely to exceed the peak of the lift curve so that lift begins to decrease. The aerodynamicist would say that the wing stalled, but in some airplanes the pilot might say "the bottom dropped out" as the nose dropped and the plane began a dive. In this situation the onset of stall has had a regenerative feedback effect. When the lift peak is exceeded, and recirculation begins to decrease, the capacity of passing flow to oppose boundary layer buildup by dragging it rearward is decreased. Thus recirculation decrease may cause further recirculation decrease very rapidly, so that the plane begins a dive.

An airfoil which has such a stall characteristic is said to have hysteresis in its lift curve. Proper lift can be regained by first decreasing the angle of attack, as may be automatic in the dive, and reinstating lift at a lower level.

76

Figure 6.3 illustrates drag effects in relation to airspeed. As airspeed is reduced, a point is reached where further reduction produces increasing total drag. If an airplane lacks sufficient engine thrust to overcome increasing drag as airspeed decreases, it may not be able to maintain level flight even though it may be operating above stall. This condition, characterized by sinking flight with full power and a nose-high attitude, is referred to as getting "behind the power curve." This applies especially to jet aircraft which lack the increased thrust at lower airspeeds characteristic of propeller driven craft. To recover from this condition, the angle of attack must be decreased in order to reduce induced drag and regain flying speed.

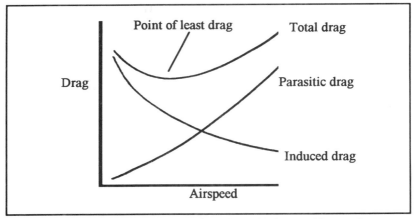

Figure 6.3 **Airplane Drag Components in Relation to Airspeed**

Total drag, represented by the uppermost plot, consists of parasitic and induced drags combined. Induced drag decreases as airspeed increases, while parasitic drag increases with airspeed.

Ground Effect

Early in flight training a student learns that, during landing flare, an airplane may tend to continue gliding a few feet above the runway without settling onto its landing gear. The apparent greater efficiency of flight near the ground is said to be due to *ground effect*.

Ground effect is due to more efficient recirculation recovery when operating in close proximity to the surface, for reasons illustrated in Figures 6.4 and 6.5. As vertical distance between wing and surface becomes less during landing, the recirculation path becomes more vertically narrow and restricted so that lateral loss lessens.

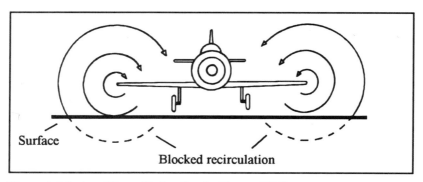

Figure 6.4 **Lateral Loss Reduction in Ground Effect**

When operating near the surface, lateral recirculation loss is impeded in the restrictive, shallow lateral path between wing and surface. The surface is represented above by the heavy line. Blocked recirculation is represented by the dashed lines below the surface.

The forward recirculation path likewise becomes narrowed, but there is a compensating effect of downwash behind the wing impacting on the surface and operating as a sort of *momentum curtain* (consult hovercraft literature) to sweep air forward below wing level. Increased lift and reduced drag then tend to make an airplane *float*, or reduce its rates of descent and deceleration.

Ground effect helps in making smooth landings but adds to landing distance. In takeoff, ground effect diminishes as distance from the surface increases. If lift-off is accomplished before airspeed is sufficient for flight out of ground effect, an airplane may stall a few feet above the ground. A lightly loaded Piper Warrior, for example, operating "behind the power curve" in takeoff with full up elevator, will repeatedly lift off and resettle to the ground so that it becomes necessary to reduce up elevator in order to gain flying speed and avoid running off the end of the runway.

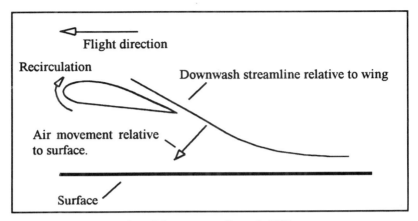

Figure 6.5 **Near-surface Momentum Curtain Effect.**

In ground effect, although the forward recirculation path is vertically narrowed, downwash behind the wing impacts upon the surface and acts as a forward-moving *momentum curtain,* sweeping air before it so as to maintain forward recirculation.

Recirculation Precession

Figure 6.6 illustrates directions of recirculation around the path of wing tip travel. Recirculation is driven by pressure gradients produced in downwash acceleration. Air accelerates outward in all directions from the higher pressure region beneath a wing, and upward and inward to the reduced pressure region above. We shall refer to forward and rearward directions as longitudinal since they are parallel to the flight path. Lateral directions are outward, upward and inward.

Air movements include combined lateral and longitudinal components. The recirculation plane at any position along the wingtip path precesses in response to changing direction of pressure gradients until at some distance behind the craft recirculation is essentially lateral.

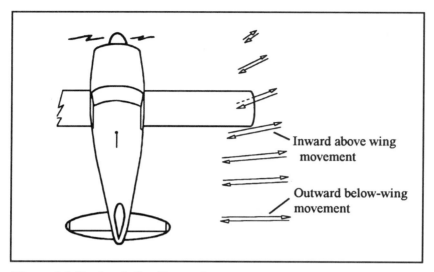

Figure 6.6 **Recirculation Precession**

Movement created in still air by a passing wing is driven by the pressure differential between the above-wing region and the below-wing region. Ahead of the wing, air is accelerated outward from the below-wing region of increased pressure in circulatory movement, and inward toward the above-wing region of decreased pressure. Ahead of mid-wing position, recirculation is purely longitudinal, but ahead of wing outer regions, recirculation develops angularly with both lateral and longitudinal components. As the wing passes, pressure forces cause recirculation paths to *precess* toward becoming more nearly lateral.

Flows Convergence and Recirculation Sourcing

In addition to precession of recirculation patterns as a wing passes, flows also converge behind a wing, as indicated in Figure 6.7. This is consequence of air acceleration into the above-wing reduced pressure region. Inward momentum continues to produce convergence to some distance aft of the wing. Thus downwash movement is more concentrated aft of the mid-wing position because of convergence, and also because pressures of wing outer span regions are relieved more by lateral loss. It follows that, since downwash is more concentrated aft of the mid-wing position, that recirculation sourcing, or downwash re-divergence, is also more concentrated there.

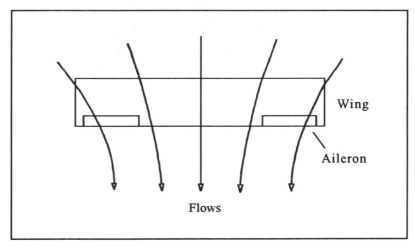

Figure 6.7 **Upper Surface Flow Convergence**

Illustrated in perspective of passing flow over a stationary wing, above-wing flows, reacting to above wing pressure reduction, converge aft of the wing to produce a concentration of downwash momentum aft of the wing mid-section. From this convergence, below-wing flows re-diverge laterally and forward into circulation around the wing, and into trailing vortices along the lines of passage of the wing ends. Convergence angularity is related to lift coefficient. As compared to normal flight the convergence is exaggerated above for illustration purposes.

Upwash is more concentrated ahead of the mid-wing region because of its proximity to the recirculation sourcing center, and because relative loss of downwash into lateral paths is greater in wing outer regions, where shorter loss paths have less mass opposition to flow acceleration. Lift is therefore more concentrated in the rectangular wing mid-span region, with the result that stall occurs there first as the lift coefficient is increased. The outer span regions, having less lift loading concentration, may remain unstalled with good aileron effectiveness for roll control. Thus a plain rectangular wing has an inherent margin of safety for avoiding spins. For wings other than plain rectangular, lift distribution and stall characteristics differ.

Although a plain rectangular wing is a good choice for construction simplicity, safety and cost, it may not be the best for weight minimization, fuel efficiency, or control responsiveness. In following sections we shall be considering wing design variations, and features of *sweep, washout, taper, slots, spoilers, vortex generators, fences* and *flaps,* and how they affect performance.

Stop Abusing Bernoulli!
How Airplanes Really Fly

VII. WING ELEMENTS

Wing Tip Variations

Because the lateral recirculation path is shortest at a wing tip, recirculation loss is more concentrated there. Understandably, there is much interest in reducing tip loss, and for this purpose a number of variations have evolved in wing tip designs. Generally these have the effect of increasing the lengths of lateral recirculation paths. In addition, most recover tip recirculation energy to generate forward thrust. The simplest, and one of the earliest efforts to inhibit tip loss, was to mount vertical flat plates on the wing ends, as in Figure 7.1. On some airplanes, the Cessna 310 for example, external fuel tanks are attached to the wing tips, thus establishing fuel storage as well as increasing lateral loss path length around the tips..

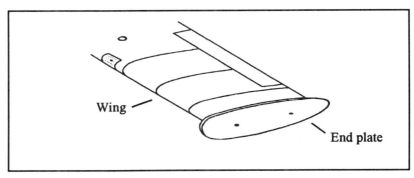

Figure 7.1 **Wing End Plate**

Wing end plates are sometimes used to lengthen the paths of lateral recirculation loss around wing tips.

Several tip designs recover tip recirculation energy in the form of forward thrust, as well as increase the length of the tip recirculation path. An example is illustrated in Figure 7.2. Sometimes these are referred to as a *winglets*.

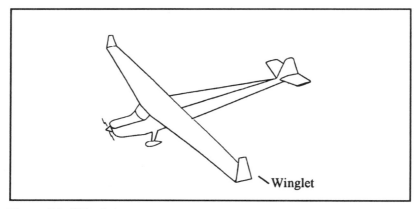

Figure 7.2 **Winglets**

Vertical wingtip additions, which may be either upturned or downturned, improve wing efficiency by increasing the path length for recirculation loss. In addition, if well designed, they provide some forward thrust as they intercept lateral tip recirculation and redirect it rearward.

If part of the lateral recirculation is intercepted and redirected more rearwardly by a vertical tip section there is a resulting rearward increase in air momentum, and consequently a forward thrust associated with leading edge suction of the vertical section. Lift is also improved by increase of path length for recirculation loss. Recirculation loss would remain at winglet ends, but of lesser magnitude than without winglets. If the vertical sections were made horizontal as additions to span, leading edge thrust would still be created and lift force, instead of being lateral on vertical sections, would be advantageously upward. A disadvantage would exist in greater space requirement for ground handling of the wider span, and the wing bending moment due to cantilevered loading would be greater.

A stalled vertical tip section would not be very effective in improving aerodynamic efficiency. Thus a winglet must be of adequate chord length to accommodate the load without stall. If the primary purpose of a vertical section is to improve low speed lift and reduce takeoff and landing distances, it would require a greater chord than it would if intended only for reducing cruise drag.

Taper

A cantilevered wing requires greatest strength at its root, with decreasing strength needed at points farther out. Required strength with least structural weight can be achieved with taper so that the wing has greatest chord and thickness at the root where forces are greatest. Other advantages are that the airplane roll rate may be faster because of less outer span mass and damping, and lift is more concentrated around mid-span so that lateral vortices loss around wing ends may be less as compared to a rectangular wing of the same aspect ratio. The term *effective aspect ratio* denotes the effect of taper on loss into "induced drag.".

A potential problem with taper is that of outer span stall with loss of aileron effectiveness. Although lift on a basic tapered wing decreases with distance from the root, it does not decrease in proportion to decrease in chord. Recirculation diverges outward from the more intense region of the longer chord middle portion of the span so that the outer span regions may intercept greater upwash concentration in proportion to chord than do the mid span regions, as illustrated in Figure 7.3. The result, for a sharply tapered wing, is that lift concentration, in terms of lift loading per unit area, is greater in the outer span regions where stall may first occur with loss of aileron effectiveness. Thus a disadvantage of a sharply tapered wing may be predisposition to abrupt spin entry followed by difficult recovery.

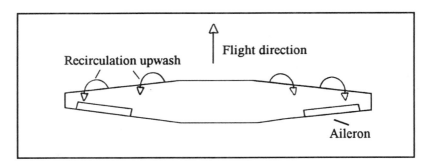

Figure 7.3 **Tapered Wing Loading**

Recirculation from the longer chord mid-span region diverges forward and laterally to increase the concentration of upwash interception and loading in the shorter chord outer span regions. With increasing lift, more heavily loaded outer span areas may stall first, causing loss of aileron control.

Stall Inhibiting Techniques

Several techniques can be employed to delay outer span stall in order to preserve aileron effectiveness of tapered wings. The most common is that of *washout* wherein the wing is *twisted* so that the angle of attack is reduced in outer regions, as illustrated in Figure 7.4.

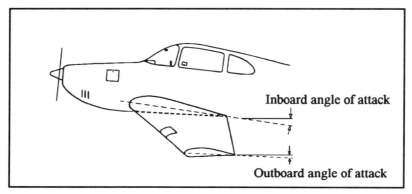

Figure 7.4 **Washout**

To reduce the tendency of tapered wings to stall first in the outboard regions, they may be designed with *twist* or *washout* so that the outer region angle of attack is less than that farther inboard.

Stall may also be delayed by increasing air velocity adjacent to the upper surface boundary layer. One means of accomplishing this is by addition of slots near the wing leading edges, as illustrated in Figure 7.5, usually ahead of the ailerons. On some airplanes slots are open only during low speed operation or at high angle of attack. Opening may be forced by an actuator mechanism; or they may be passively forced open by aerodynamic forces.

The WWII F-86 fighter plane is an example of an airplane with slots opened by aerodynamic forces. As the angle of attack increases it causes the leading edge stagnation line, where flow divides between upper and lower surfaces, to move downward. With sufficient downward movement, forward thrust exerted on a movable leading edge section, called a *slat*, causes the slat to move forward so that the slot is opened.

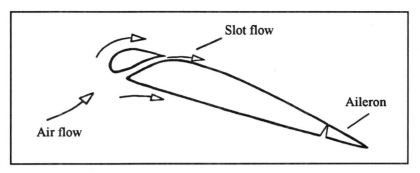

Figure 7.5 **Wing Slot**

A wing slot channels air flow from the higher pressure leading edge stagnation line region to the upper surface so as to increase flow velocity adjacent to the upper surface boundary layer. Rearward drag force exerted by passing air on the boundary layer is thus increased, and stall is delayed to higher angle of attack. If the leading edge section is movable to open the slot it is called a *slat*.

Upper surface flow velocity increase may also be accomplished by providing air from pumps through ducts to aft-facing slots as indicated in Figure 7.6. This method is not widely employed because of complexity and pump power requirements.

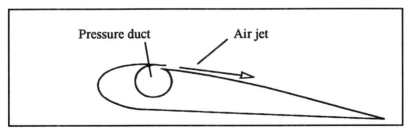

Figure 7.6 **Blown wing**

A *blown wing* has high velocity air forced rearward over the upper surface to aid in boundary layer energization and delay stall to higher angle of attack.

Mixing of passing flow into the boundary layer by means of turbulence generation from intentional surface roughening was mentioned in an earlier section. Near-surface turbulence may also be generated by short vanes attached in perpendicular orientation to the wing surfaces. The vanes, acting as small airfoils, produce small trailing vortices which energize and remove boundary layer buildup. Such vanes may be seen on upper wing surfaces of a variety of airplanes.

Another method of reducing boundary layer buildup is to remove it into the wing by suction through a great number of small perforations in an upper wing surface. Like a blown wing, this requires heavy, complex pumping systems. Although proven to work, suction removal has had very limited application.

Wing Sweep

Most jet airplanes have wings angled rearward in relation to the roots in what is known as *rearward sweep*. This usually is for reduction of drag at speeds approaching that of sound. However, sweep also influences aerodynamic performance at low speeds. For example, it is known that rearward sweep contributes to earlier stall of outboard regions, and conversely, forward sweep inhibits outboard region stall.

Differing stall effects with fore and aft sweep can be explained in relation to recirculation concentration. A uniform rectangular wing stalls first in its mid-section, leaving outer regions functional with effective ailerons for roll control. This is because recirculation upwash concentration is greater in the mid-section, and outer regions are unloaded more by lateral loss. These effects can be influenced with sweep. As illustrated in Figure 7.7, rearward sweep moves the wing mid-section relatively farther from recirculation sourcing. Thus upwash concentration and loading are lessened in the mid-section as compared to the outer sections, and with reduced mid-wing loading, stall is inhibited so that outer span regions may stall earlier with loss of roll control, especially with taper. The tendency is usually corrected with washout and perhaps some other features such as slots or other boundary layer energization methods.

Forward sweep, also illustrated, moves the wing root relatively nearer to recirculation sourcing as compared to the outer regions so that outer region stall is delayed. Thus forward sweep could be used to offset, at least partially, the effect of taper. Not many airplanes have been built with

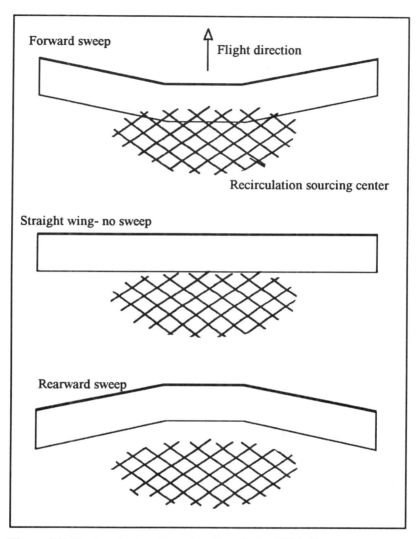

Figure 7.7 **Recirculation Sourcing Proximity With Sweep**

Although the downwash convergence-redivergence region has no defin-
able borders, we can symbolically represent the region of greatest concentration of forward redivergence sourcing as above in the crosshatched
areas. Relative proximity of convergence-redivergence concentration to
mid-span and wing outer regions differs with sweep. With forward
sweep, the ratio of mid-span loading to outer span loading is increased
by closer proximity of the concentration region to the mid-section, as
compared to the outer span regions. With rearward sweep, mid-span
loading is lessened in relation to outer span loading.

obvious forward sweep. A deterrent of concern is that of the effect of wing flexing on angle of attack. As forward-swept wing tips flex upward under loading there is effectively an increase in angle of attack. With a sudden gust-induced lift increase, resultant angle of attack increase produces further lift increase. Structural stresses and ride discomfort may be exacerbated unless the wing is sufficiently rigid to minimize distortion.

With rearward sweep, upward wingtip flexing reduces angle of attack, thus reducing loading. This tends to relieve transient stresses in turbulence, and may reduce passenger discomfort to some degree. The effect of structural distortion interaction with aerodynamic performance as a subject of study is known as *aeroelasticity*.

Aft Region Stall

Either forward or rearward sweep may tend to promote aft region early stall. Forward sweep tends to promote earlier stall of the mid-section, which is farther aft. This may promote pitch-up, and in turn, greater stall. Rearward sweep tends to promote earlier stall of outboard sections, again farther aft, also tending to promote pitch-up and greater stall. Whether or not a significant problem is incurred would depend on the degree of sweep and other factors such as washout, taper, boundary layer control and effectiveness of pitch control systems.

Spanwise Flow

Another consideration with sweep is that it may promote lateral or spanwise flow of boundary layer air along the wing surface. Forces involved in spanwise flow are illustrated in Figure 7.8.

The position of least pressure on an airfoil upper surface is along a line essentially parallel to the leading edge. From this line rearward there is a gradient of pressure rise, perpendicular to the line of minimum pressure, which exerts force on the boundary layer. On a straight wing, force of this pressure gradient is directly forward, but is directly opposed by drag of rearward passing flow. Thus in flight of a straight wing, directly opposing boundary layer forces have no lateral component or result. In the case of

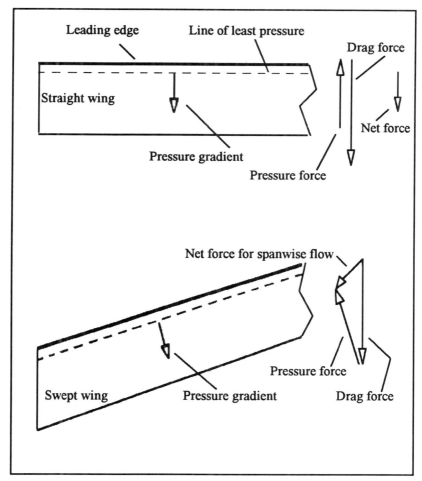

Figure 7.8 **Sweep and Forces Affecting Boundary Layer Flow**

In the upper straight wing case, rearward force exerted on the boundary layer by viscous drag of passing flow is in direct opposition to forward force exerted on the boundary layer by the rearward pressure gradient. There is no lateral force on the boundary layer. In the lower case with sweep, the combination of pressure gradient and viscous drag from passing flow add to produce net force in the downspan direction, as indicated in the force diagram at the right. Resulting spanwise movement of the boundary layer builds in depth, and contributes to greater flow separation problems as compared to a straight wing.

a swept wing, the line of minimum pressure is not perpendicular to passing flow, and hence the aft pressure gradient is not parallel to flow as it was with the straight wing. The combined forces of pressure gradient and drag add with a net lateral component which promotes downwspan flow and greater buildup of the boundary layer. This problem may be dealt with by adding vortex generating vanes to break up and disperse spanwise flows, or short sheet metal *fences*, oriented along the desired flow paths to block lateral flow.

With a forward-swept wing, as indicated in Figure 7.9, the spanwise flow problem is further compounded in the wing end regions by directions of precessing recirculation. Oppositely, rearward sweep can better orient wing end regions in relation to precessing recirculation.

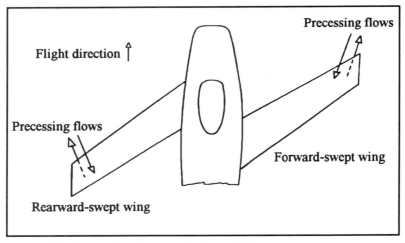

Figure 7.9 **Precessing Recirculation with Sweep**

On a swept wing, flow direction is not perpendicular to the airfoil line of minimum pressure, which is basically parallel to the leading edge. This results in spanwise boundary layer flow and buildup. With forward sweep of the right wing, precessing flow direction in the tip region is offset farther from perpendicular to the line of minimum pressure, so that spanwise boundary layer flow is further aggravated. Rearward sweep of the left wing, on the other hand, more nearly orients the minimum pressure line perpendicular to precessing flow in the wing end region so as to inhibit spanwise buildup.

92

Angles of flow in the wing end regions vary with lift coefficient, and hence vary with airspeed, loading and air density. Where lift coefficients are less, recirculation convergence angles would be less. Thus the direction of sweep of wing ends is of greatest influence on flow separation during takeoff and landing, in "high G" maneuvers, and in high altitude operation.

Combined Fore and Aft Sweep

Forward sweep moves recirculation sourcing nearer the mid-span region, as was illustrated in Figure 7.7. In doing so it concentrates more lift around mid-span where lateral losses are less. Thus there is potential for greater efficiency with forward sweep. On the other hand, rearward sweep has potential for better performance in the precessing flows of wing end regions, and does not require the structural rigidity of forward sweep. The straight wing is, of course, a compromise between relative factors of forward and rearward sweep, but another compromise is in combining the advantage of forward sweep in the mid-section with the advantage of outer sections rearward sweep, as Mother Nature has done through evolution in many species of birds.

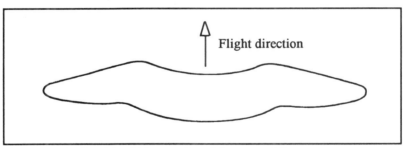

Figure 7.10 **Combined Forward and Rearward Sweep**

Many bird species have wing planforms similar to the outline above. Presumably this combination of forward sweep in the mid-region and rearward sweep in the outer regions is advantageous for survival.

Dihedral

Airplane wings, especially those of low wing craft, are usually designed with upward slope in the outboard direction, so that the middle is lower than the ends, as in Figure 7.11. This characteristic is known as *dihedral*. There are different reasons for dihedral. On low wing planes, dihedral provides more ground clearance for avoiding wingtip strike during landing and takeoff. On high wing planes, dihedral allows better in-flight lateral visibility for sighting other aircraft. With both high wing and low wing planes however, dihedral affects flight characteristics.

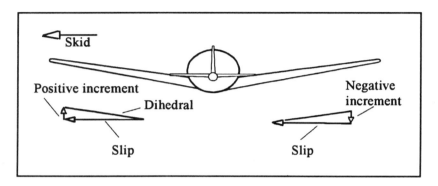

Figure 7.11 **Dihedral**

In the illustration above, the low-wing airplane is slipping or skidding to the left. In left movement, the inclined left wing has an added positive increment of angle of attack, while the wing opposite has a decreased angle of attack increment. Resulting lift differential, greater on the left wing, rolls the craft away from the slip, or toward the right as seen above.

When a plane is turned with rudder alone, it tends to slip, or skid laterally. Wings with dihedral develop differential lift in a slip or a crosswind, tending to roll in opposite direction to the direction of slip. A high degree of dihedral is sometimes built into free flight model airplanes which have no ailerons. With sufficient dihedral, steering can be accomplished quite well with rudder alone. When rudder produces a skid, dihedral effect produces roll into the turn.

Too much dihedral may produce *Dutch roll* if a plane rolls past the point of stopping a slip, and develops a new slip in the opposite direction resulting again in excess roll. The process may continue with yawing, rolling oscillation. In occupied real airplanes Dutch roll instability increases pilot work load and can be nauseating.

94

Even without dihedral, wings have a dihedral-like effect. As illustrated in Figure 7.12, wingtip circulation in combination with a lateral flow component, as in a sideslip, produces lift in accordance with the Kutta-Joukowski theorem, or in other terms, a greater lift is obtained on the wingtip which is moving into recirculation upwash and less on the tip moving away from it. The effects are opposite at upwind and downwind wing tips.

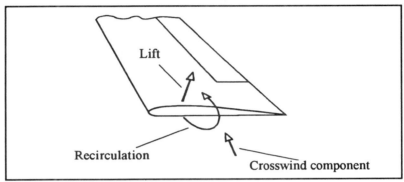

Figure 7.12 **Wingtip Kutta-Joukowski Lift**

Wingtip recirculation, in combination with flow across the tip recirculation axis, produces lift in accordance with the Kutta-Joukowski theorem. In the illustration above, wingtip recirculation from below to above the wing is subjected to lateral flow, which may be from a crosswind or from lateral slipping. Resultant lift adds to that of wing operation at the upwind end, and detracts from lift at the downwind end.

Rearward sweep also produces differential lift in a slip. As sideslip develops, the leading edge of the swept back wing on the side of the direction of skid becomes more nearly normal to the direction of travel, so that lift is increased. At the other wing there is an opposite effect. Resultant lift differential then rolls the plane in the direction to stop the slip. A forward-swept wing would have an opposite effect.

Ailerons

Ailerons are employed on most airplanes to differentially adjust wing downwash angles so as to affect relative wing lifts for purposes of roll control. Roll control is needed to keep the airplane in an upright position, but is also needed to bank the airplane for turns.

Coordinated turns with ailerons usually require rudder application to correct *adverse yaw,* a condition in which rolling into a bank produces yaw of the airplane into the opposite turn direction, as indicated in Figure 7.13.

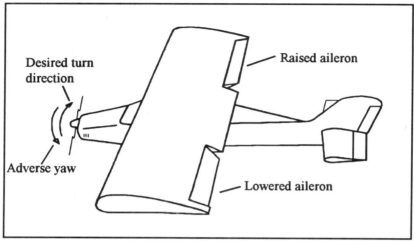

Figure 7.13 **Adverse Yaw**

As an airplane is rolled into a bank for turning, it tends to yaw in the opposite direction.

Lift force is perpendicular to the direction of wing travel through the air. In roll the rising wing is traveling an inclined path, with the result that lift, perpendicular to the path, is slightly inclined rearward. On the opposite side, lift of the descending wing is inclined slightly forward. The difference in lift directions tends to pull the descending wing forward and the ascending wing rearward so as to yaw the airplane in direction opposite to that desired.

Spoilers

Spoilers, an alternative to ailerons for roll control, operate by interfering with circulation. Spoilers are drag devices, and because they are located on upper wing surfaces, they oppose circulation when deployed. Unlike ailerons, which are located in wing trailing edges, spoilers are normally located farther forward as illustrated in Figure 7.14.

96

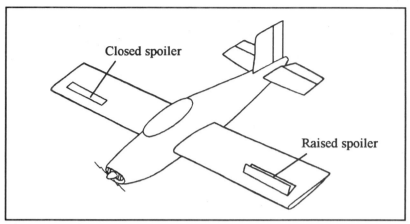

Figure 7.14 **Spoilers**

Spoilers, through drag, reduce circulation and lift when raised. Operated independently they are used as roll control devices. Operated together they produce drag and reduce lift. Sailplanes usually use spoilers to control speed in descent, and to spoil lift for good braking at touchdown.

If located in the aft portion of wings, spoilers must be raised higher to be effective than would be required if they were forward-mounted, in order to extend above the boundary layer and separated flow and remain effective, especially at low speeds when separated flow is deep. When mounted in the forward regions, where there is little flow separation, they must seal reasonably well when retracted to prevent air leakage which would interfere with efficient lift generation. In sealing they must also be resistant to freezing in closed position with consequent loss of use.

Spoilers have a definite advantage in turn coordination. For example, raising a left spoiler will produce left bank due to left wing lift reduction, and simultaneous left yaw due to spoiler drag.

Flaps

In takeoff and landing, it is necessary to operate at low speed with high lift coefficient. During such operation, outer span region lift and aileron control be must be maintained. Thus this is the time of greatest need for washout and camber, and on most airplanes both are effectively increased for low speed operation by deployment of *flaps,* illustrated in Figure 7.15.

97

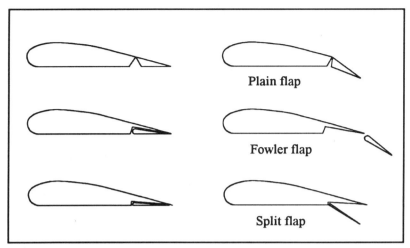

Figure 7.15 **Flaps**

Three basic types of flaps are shown above. On the left the flaps are shown in cruise mode while on the right they are in deployed mode as for takeoff or landing. Of these types, the *Fowler flap* provides best performance but is also the most costly because it requires a track mechanism for support and travel. On large airplanes, flaps are usually more complex, sometimes with multiple extensions in tandem.

One of the simplest flap designs, as found on some small Piper aircraft, consists of hinged trailing edge sections on each side near the passenger cabin. These function to increase wing mid-section camber and downwash angle, and increase lift in relation to airframe attitude, or angle of inclination relative to the flight path. In effect, flap deployment produces wing washout as the wing mid-section angle of attack is increased in comparison to outer sections. All flap designs increase wing mid-section downwash angle, recirculation and lift when deployed, but *Fowler flaps* also extend trailing edges rearward to increase local chord length for a gain in wing area. In addition to permitting lower operating speed, flaps provide better over-the-nose visibility with lowered airframe attitude.

The split flap is another simple design which produces combined effects of increased trailing edge downwash angle and below-wing drag. The split flap is essentially a flat section which is held against the underside of the wing during cruise, and is pivoted downward for low speed lift and for drag during descent. It drags air forward on the wing underside, adding to recirculation, and it also increases the downwash angle.

At small degrees of deployment, increase of lift is the most noticeable effect of flaps, but with full deployment, drag becomes very apparent. Hence, if used for takeoff, flaps are normally partially extended so as to reduce the takeoff speed requirement and preserve aileron effectiveness, but on landing are fully extended when drag is needed to dissipate gravitational energy of descent so as to maintain desired aircraft speed. On some airplanes the drag of fully extended flaps is so great that level flight cannot be maintained even with full engine power. A prudent pilot will remember this when aborting a full flaps landing.

Any below-wing drag adds to recirculation. Thus energy consumed in below-wing drag of landing gear is partially regained in the lift process through upwash recovery. Partial energy recovery may permit high drag loads to be carried beneath wings. Ranchers have been known to carry hay bales lashed to lightplane struts for feeding of snowbound cattle. Other individuals have been seen carrying bicycles lashed to struts. Needless to say, FAA does not approve these activities. Such loads must be reasonably balanced in opposing side drag in order to permit rudder control. Loss of a load on only one side could produce an exciting yaw situation.

Flaperons and Elevons

Sometimes aileron and flap functions are combined in continuous hinged surfaces, called *flaperons,* which extend nearly full span along wing trailing edges. Operated differentially, with one being raised as the other is lowered, they act as ailerons for roll control. Lowered together they perform as flaps for increasing drag and lift, or they may be raised above normal trailing edge level in upward *reflex* to reduce cruise drag. Flap and aileron functions can be accommodated simultaneously through a mechanical mixing arrangement into which aileron and flap controls connect, so that the aileron function is preserved even when the flap function is in use.

A possible disadvantage of the flaperon arrangement is that, since the flap function is effectively full-span, there is no resultant washout increase effect like that achieved with conventional flaps. Thus, outer span early stall may not be as well inhibited.

Flaperons are often mounted below wing trailing edges, rather than as part of the trailing edges. This arrangement, illustrated in Figure 7.16, is said to be more effective at high lift coefficient, as when operating at low speed during takeoff and landing, because the flaperons operate in below wing flow which is less affected by boundary layer buildup.

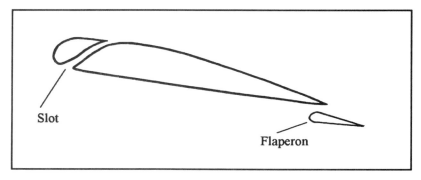

Figure 7.16 **Flaperon and Slot Configuration**

Opposite side flaperons are lowered simultaneously for the flap function, and are operated differentially for the aileron function. The slot effectiveness is enhanced by back pressure from flap function so that the combination is quite effective.

Flaperons are reported to work well in combination with leading edge slots. When the flap function is operative the back pressure adds to slot flow so that the slots become more effective. This is a feature of some Zenith aircraft designs by Chris Heintz, which have eighteen percent thick wings. Maximum lift coefficients achieved are reported as 3.1.

Elevons, are similar to flaperons, but combine elevator and aileron functions on "tail-less," usually *delta wing* airplanes. Like flaperons, elevons operate together for pitch control, while for roll control they are operated differentially.

100

Stop Abusing Bernoulli!
How Airplanes Really Fly

VIII. CONFIGURATION

Working parts of an airplane typically include wings with ailerons, horizontal stabilizer-elevator, vertical stabilizer-rudder, engine-propeller, and landing gear. Design, number and arrangement of these components, varies with airplane *configuration*.

Stability and Feedback

To be stable and controllable, an airplane needs some degree of negative feedback in its control functions, so that change produces forces resisting the change. A system in which change produces forces for further change is unstable. As an example of an unstable system, consider a taildragger airplane, which has its center of mass behind the main landing gear.

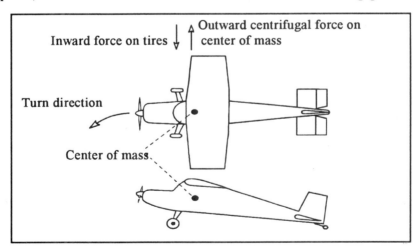

Figure 8.1 **Taildragger Ground Instability**

In a turn, outward force on the center of mass and inward force on the main gear form a couple tending to force an increasingly tighter turn. This process, if unchecked, can cause *groundloop,* a quick uncontrolled increase in turn rate perhaps resulting in wingtip strike and aircraft damage.

The light taildragger usually has a castering tail wheel, spring-coupled to the rudder, which deflects in steering angle under rudder pedal force and lateral force of wind or turning acceleration. In order for the plane to stand on its main gear and tail wheel, its center of mass, or center of gravity, C.G., must be between these locations. This is the source of instability.

In a turn on the ground, outward centrifugal force tends to swing the tail in the direction of increasing turn rate. The tendency for turning force to promote increasing turn rate constitutes positive feedback instability. In learning to operate a taildragger on the ground, one must develop automatic reflexes for applying turn-opposing rudder force with proper timing to override the positive feedback, and obtain desired direction without overshoot.

The more common tricycle gear, as in Figure 8.2, has its C.G. located between nose and main gear, and when operating with little weight on the nose wheel, or with the nose wheel off the runway, has stability associated with negative feedback. In a turn, surface traction of the main gear, together with momentum of the airplane mass acting at the C.G., forms a couple which tends to turn the airplane into straight line travel. Tricycle gear is thus more forgiving of sideslip during touchdown, when accelerative force tends to turn the plane into the direction of travel, rather than into an increasing turn like the taildragger. Insurance companies recognize the better ground stability of the tricycle geared plane, which it provides with lower rates. Learning to control the taildragger on the ground, however, is more challenging and interesting than is the tricycle gear.

Tricycle gear planes, when operated on the runway at or near flight speed with heavy forward wheel pressure, may lift the main gear and run only on the nose gear. This action is called *wheelbarrowing*. The C.G. is aft of the nose wheel, which in wheelbarrowing is the only runway contact. If a turn is initiated, outward centrifugal force on the center of mass, and inward force on the nose wheel, form a couple which tends to increase the turn rate. This condition of positive feedback instability can result in loss of control, in a manner similar to that of the taildragger.

With luck, the airspeed required for wheelbarrowing may produce sufficient vertical stabilizer effectiveness to prevent groundlooping. However, this is a situation to be avoided.

Weight, Balance, and Pitch

For any airplane in stable, straight and level flight, the total of aerodynamic forces of lift, thrust, and drag can be represented as a single upward vector equal to, but opposite in direction to aircraft weight. We can think of these vectors as acting on the aircraft center of gravity (C.G.), as in Figure 8.2. If the C.G. moves forward of this position, the resulting couple will tend to pitch the aircraft attitude downward. Conversely, aft C.G. movement will produce pitch up. This is the method of pitch control of a hang glider in which the C.G. is shifted in fore and aft directions by body movement of the pilot.

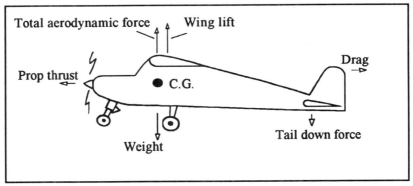

Figure 8.2 **Total Aerodynamic Force**

In stable flight, thrust and drag forces are equal but opposite in direction, and lift and weight forces are also equal but opposite. In the above illustration, thrust and drag forces are not co-linear, and thus constitute a couple which produces a small pitch-up tendency. Tail down force balances the pitch down tendency resulting from offset between weight force and wing lift minus the small upward pitch force from offset between thrust and drag. Total lift is wing lift minus negative lift of the horizontal stabilizer. Total aerodynamic force, including lift, drag and thrust, operates on the center of gravity to hold the airplane in level flight with no net pitching moment.

In normal level flight of a conventional aft-tail airplane, coincidence of total aerodynamic force with the C.G. is controlled by the elevator, which adjusts negative, or downward, lift of the horizontal stabilizer. When trimmed for level flight, a speed increase will increase both upward wing lift and downward stabilizer force, thereby producing a pitch upward. Oppositely, a decrease from level trim speed will produce downward pitch. In either case the speed change produces descent or climb which tends to bring the airspeed back toward the trimmed level. Elevator trim thus functions primarily as a speed control, while climb and descent result from engine power variations. An increase in power will begin to increase speed, which in turn will produce pitch-up for climb. Oppositely, a power decrease will cause a pitch down for descent.

Pitch change does not usually hold airspeed absolutely constant. Some single-engine conventional aft-stabilizer airplanes may increase speed somewhat as power is reduced, and decrease speed as power is increased. This is because of the propeller thrust line and propeller wake effect on the horizontal stabilizer. Decreased power reduces wake velocity across the horizontal stabilizer, and thus reduces stabilizer down force. Pitch down then occurs, with stable flight occurring at some angle of descent which may yield higher than level trimmed speed. Conversely, an addition of power when trimmed for level flight produces greater propwash and stabilizer down force which may produce climb speed less than level trim speed. This assumes that the pilot takes no corrective action. Normal pilot action is to re-trim the elevator-stabilizer for desired flight attitude when the throttle setting is changed.

Because downward force of the horizontal stabilizer opposes wing lift, which must then be increased in compensation, there is some drag penalty. This is minimized if the plane is loaded so as to have a C.G. near the aft limit. With weight farther aft, the stabilizer down force requirement is lessened, hence wing lift is equally lessened. Together the reductions reduce overall drag.

With load too far aft, the stabilizing relationship of upward wing force and downward tail force is diminished or upset. Resulting instability may make control difficult or outside the range of human

104

reaction capability. Stall and spin may be entered quite easily with recovery difficult or impossible. However, with fast computer assist stabilization preventing operation into stall, it can be possible to maintain control even with a neutral or upward-lifting aft stabilizer. The horizontal stabilizer of the F-16 fighter, for example, which produces positive lift, is operated by computer with programmed stabilizing feedback.

Although the conventional aft horizontal stabilizer produces downward force which adds to the wing lift requirement, it also produces forward thrust, as illustrated in Figure 8.3.

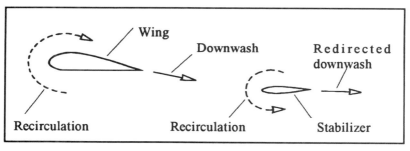

Figure 8.3 Horizontal Stabilizer Thrust

Downwash behind the wing is redirected more rearwardly by the conventional stabilizer. Downward air momentum is reduced so that downward thrust results. Rearward momentum is increased so that forward thrust results. Note that circulations are in opposite directions with opposite directions of lift.

Part of the wing downwash is redirected more rearwardly by the horizontal stabilizer, and in this redirection, rearward air momentum of the airstream is increased. As required by Newton's laws of physics, forward thrust accompanies the rearward momentum increase. This thrust, appearing at the leading edge of the stabilizer, is produced in the same manner that leading edge thrust is produced by redirection of upwash at the wing leading edge. The horizontal stabilizer thereby partially recovers the additional energy expended by the wing in producing lift to compensate for the stabilizer down force requirement.

For this recovery to be efficient, the horizontal stabilizer should be designed as an airfoil, rather than as just part of the "tailfeathers." Some older lightplanes, for example, have flat horizontal stabilizers consisting simply of bent tubing covered with fabric.

Forward thrust generation from redirection of flow is also important for a sailboat, not only for the sail, but also for the keel, which operates in water but is often designed much like an airfoil. As the boat tends to skid under lateral force of the sails, a properly designed keel generates recirculation and useful forward thrust, just as does an airfoil or wing.

Canard

Canard is a French word meaning duck. The term came to be applied to airplanes having horizontal stabilizer-elevator systems mounted ahead of the main wing or wings, as in Figure 8.4. Because of the outstretched stabilizer mounting arm, appearance was likened to that of a duck in flight with outstretched neck.

Figure 8.4 **Canard Airplane**

The pitch control surface, or horizontal stabilizer, of a *canard* (duck) airplane is mounted at or near the front of the airframe. Although the canard can produce good performance, its potential for dangerous positive feedback instability requires more expertise in design as compared to the conventional aft stabilizer.

106

It is sometimes claimed that canard airplanes are inherently more efficient, as compared to conventional aft-tail designs, because canard surface lift is in an upward direction adding to wing lift, rather than opposing lift as does the conventional aft stabilizer. Although this claim has validity, the differences are not really so simple. A canard horizontal stabilizer is loaded rather heavily, often with low aspect ratio. Consequently, its lifting efficiency may not be great; and the main wing operates in the wake of the canard stabilizer, losing some degree of efficiency as a result of operating in disturbed flow. Also, thrust generation of the conventional aft stabilizer must be considered in the comparison.

Despite these considerations, some canard designs have demonstrated performance and efficiency greater than that of many other lightplanes. Perhaps more important than the canard configuration are the factors of rear-mounted propeller, and light, composite, purpose-oriented construction of most designs, usually intended to operate from smooth, relatively long runways and carry little baggage.

The canard stabilizer is designed so that, in normal flight conditions, boundary layer buildup effects are more pronounced than they are on the main wing. Consequently, the canard horizontal stabilizer efficiency is more sensitive to airspeed changes than is efficiency of the main wing. This relationship is the source of pitch stability. When trimmed for level flight, downward pitch will produce increased speed which will improve lift efficiency of the canard stabilizer more than it improves that of the main wing, thus resulting in pitch up toward level flight. Conversely, upward pitch will decrease speed, reduce canard stabilizer efficiency more than that of the main wing, and result in pitch down toward level flight. Thus, the forward canard stabilizer, like the more conventional aft horizontal stabilizer, tends to hold airspeed through a negative feedback process.

A problem which has plagued some canard designs is that of pitch down in rain. The forces of surface drag and aft pressure gradients which produce boundary layer buildup can also produce water buildup when operating in rain. As water flow across the surface is retarded by viscous drag, it can build in depth as its flow is opposed by the aft pressure gradient. Water accumulation effectively changes the roughness and profile of the canard airfoil, thereby affecting its aerodynamic properties. According to Dick Rutan's account in the book *Voyager*, the craft was nearly lost in the first rain it encountered in testing, when canard stabilizer lift loss caused severe pitch-down.

Some canard airplanes, including Voyager, have been modified by adding numerous tiny vertical *turbulator* or vortex generating fins on the stabilizer upper surface. The fins produce vortices which trail across the surface, and through turbulent agitation, mix water into the air flow so that it is carried away. Such a modification should not be undertaken casually. Excess increase in canard stabilizer maximum lift coefficient could upset the airplane stability with potentially disastrous results.

Yaw Control

Yaw, the rotation of an airplane around its normally vertical axis, is usually moderated by a vertical stabilizer assembly, which includes the rudder. As indicated in Figure 8.5, when the stabilizer yaws to an angle offset from the airstream, resultant aerodynamic force tends to restore the airplane heading. This heading restoration tendency, a negative feedback, also exerts a degree of opposition to rudder application for desired turns.

Yaw for turns can also be accomplished by wingtip drag devices which may consist of small movable surfaces at the end of each wing. When a drag device on the side of the direction of turn is positioned in opposition to the flowstream, drag yaws the plane in the desired direction. Some ultralight airplanes have been built with independently operable dual rudder-like drag devices, one on each of the tips of swept back wings. For a turn, the rudder on the side of the desired turn direction is deflected so as to produce both rudder action and drag, which together operate to effect the desired yaw.

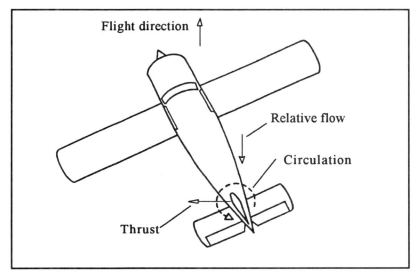

Figure 8.5 **Heading Stabilization**

More conventional airplane designs have yaw controlled by a vertical rudder-stabilizer assembly. Heading deviation, or yaw, initiated by the rudder or by turbulence, is opposed by vertical stabilizer action. This is a negative feedback effect which stabilizes airplane heading.

High Wing vs Low Wing

With a few exceptions, light planes may be classified as *high wing* or *low wing*. Passage of *mid-wing* spars through a passenger compartment takes up seating space. Thus, the wing is usually either above or below passenger level. Which position is more desirable is a matter of individual taste. Some prefer low wings for better upward visibility in turns. Others prefer high wings for downward visibility in navigation, and for the shading effect of the upper wing which reduces sunlight in the cockpit. Aside from these matters of individual taste, wing position does affect aerodynamic performance.

With a forward mounted single engine, a propeller slipstream, for the most part, passes over a low wing but under a high wing. Propwash thus enters into the recirculation around the wing, as shown in Figure 8.6.

109

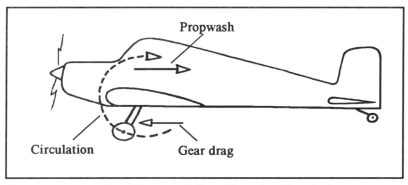

Figure 8.6 **Propeller Wake and Gear Drag In Circulation**

Circulation around an aircraft wing is affected by factors aside from wing parameters. As indicated above, the propeller wake of a low wing plane assists circulation, as does landing rear drag.

In takeoff, propwash of a low wing plane increases circulation and lift so that required ground run distance may be less. In power-off descent, the drag of a windmilling propeller opposes circulation of a low wing plane so that, in order to maintain required lift, a higher approach speed and consequent longer landing roll may be necessary. Fuselage drag, being above the wing, also detracts from circulation of the low wing plane.

The high wing plane is affected oppositely by the propeller wake. Propwash passing under the wing opposes circulation and lift during takeoff so as to increase ground run, but during descent, drag of the fuselage and a windmilling propeller contribute to circulation so that approach speed and landing roll may be less.

Biplanes

Biplanes have both high and low wings. Most successful early airplanes, including those of the Wright brothers, were biplanes. The chief advantage of a biplane is that its inter-wing bracing system provides for great strength in a light structure. Aerodynamically, as a class, biplanes are not very efficient. Circulation paths of the two wings mutually interfere, as indicated in Figure 8.7, and the inter-wing bracing system has high drag. Biplanes may have docile stall characteristics, with the upper wing stalling before the lower, but this is dependent upon relative properties of the two wings and the way they are rigged. For aerobatics, the biplane is often chosen for the structural strength of inter-wing bracing, and because the high drag permits diving maneuvers which otherwise might produce dangerously high airspeeds. Docile stall is not desired in an aerobatic show-plane which may be required to perform violent snap rolls.

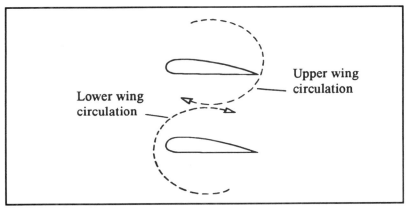

Figure 8.7 **Biplane Circulation Interference**

Circulation around biplane wings moves in opposite directions between the wings. Interference between the circulation patterns has a negative effect on performance.

Aft vs Forward Engine

In addition to circulation effects of propwash from a forward mounted engine, there is also the factor of propwash drag on the fuselage to consider when the propeller of a single engine plane is mounted at the front. Because the propeller wake increases the slipstream velocity along the fuselage, while drag increases in proportion to slipstream velocity squared, wake drag of a forward propeller is definitely a performance factor. Rear-mounted propellers potentially provide greater efficiency, except that the propeller input air may have become turbulent from effects ahead. The Cessna Skymaster

111

has two equally rated engines, one in front and one at the rear. It produces better single-engine speed and fuel economy on the rear engine than it does on the forward engine, but at least part of this is attributed to the fact that flow convergence at the rather blunt fuselage rear is poor when operating on the front engine alone. *Voyager*, a newsworthy airplane for having flown non-stop and unrefueled around the world with an engine in front and an engine at the rear, flew most of its trip on the rear engine alone for best fuel economy.

With a rear mounted engine, increased fuselage drag due to the propeller wake is avoided. There is also a potential for partial recovery of fuselage drag loss. Air is dragged forward by the fuselage so that it develops forward velocity. If this forward-moving air is intercepted by the propeller, and accelerated rearward for production of forward thrust, it will produce a greater thrust-to-power ratio than will still air encountered by a forward propeller. Thus there is potential for partial recovery of power lost in fuselage drag.

Recovery of fuselage slipstream energy, as it passes through a rear mounted propeller, would require that the affected depth of air extend out beyond perhaps a third of the propeller arc radius, because the inner portion of a propeller is rather ineffective in thrust production. Thus, for a typical rear propeller configuration, significant slipstream energy recovery is unlikely. However, the basic principle also would apply to jet airplanes, where the potential for recovery of fuselage slipstream kinetic energy through an annular air intake into a tail mounted engine could be worth considering. This would require re-thinking of the traditional separation between airframe and engine engineering, because the engine compressor would have to make up the inlet ram pressure difference in reduced velocity intake air.

Piston engines mounted at the rear are more difficult to cool, provide no impact protection in event of forced landing, and do not work easily into an overall weight and balance scheme. However, an airplane could have a forward engine with a rear propeller driven by a long shaft. This could provide rear propeller advantages while maintaining the cooling and mass location advantages of forward engine mounting.

Flapping Wing Flight

From the earliest efforts of man to fly, there has been interest in flapping wing flight. Some of the earliest experimenters attempted to emulate bird configuration and action. The challenge remains.

Flapping wings, unless varied over a very wide range of pitch angle in each flap cycle, would remain stalled and produce very little forward thrust for starting acceleration and a takeoff run. Birds have an advantage of articulated wings capable of wide ranges of pitch angle and twist, and can run on their feet to establish initial airspeed to get out of stall. For manned flapping wing flight, powered wheel propulsion could be used to get out of stall condition. The required angles of pitch variation would be inversely related to takeoff speed. A higher ground speed driven through surface traction would reduce the engineering difficulty associated with pitch variation and twist.

There is potential for greater flight efficiency with flapping wing propulsion as compared to propulsion with a rotating propeller. Power losses are associated with operation of both propellers and wings. Elimination of the propeller would eliminate propeller losses.

A practical consideration is that lift will have to be maintained sufficiently constant through each flap cycle in both upward and downward wing motion to permit some degree of pilot comfort. A pilot oscillating violently in vertical movement could not be expected to maintain control. This may be the greater challenge in manned flapping wing flight. Perhaps flapping of only outer portions of wing span would suffice for propulsion, with lift compensation during the cycle being accomplished by cycling hinged trailing edge flap-like devices on the non-flapping inboard sections.

Stop Abusing Bernoulli!
How Airplanes Really Fly

IX. DOES IT REALLY MATTER?

Thus far we have covered several aspects of airplane flight with explanations in terms of Newtonian physics without involving the Bernoulli theorem. Some would argue that this is simply another way of regarding flight principles, and doesn't change the way airplanes are designed, built and operated. Thus they would argue that there is no need for explanations we have covered.

A counter-argument would be that there is a definite need, for popular explanations of basic flight principles are false and misleading, and though students may "learn" them as required, they are likely lose respect for learning institutions as a consequence. We cannot know how many students have given up interest in subjects related to aviation, and even in basic science, as they recognized that they were being taught falsehood dressed in sophisticated mathematics as scientific fact. We also cannot know what advances in aviation we have delayed by not teaching genuine understanding of flight principles.

Lift From Engine Waste Heat?

Let's consider an idea of Darryl Phillips, of Sallisaw, Oklahoma. Mr. Phillips had an idea that if the bottom surface of a wing were made to dissipate waste engine heat, it might add to wing lift because of boundary layer expansion and resulting downward displacement of passing air. How might we evaluate such a concept?

If we look at this idea from a perspective of Newtonian principles, it is clear that heating of the air passing a wing lower surface would indeed cause it to expand downward, and the downward acceleration would produce upward reaction force as lift. The next consideration is of how much lift might result. We could assume it would be insignificant and abandon the thought, but it is not difficult to do an approximate calculation based on the fact that lift is a function of downwash angle.

Adding thickness to the lower surface boundary layer by thermal expansion would effectively increase the downward angle of deflection of passing air mass, as indicated below:

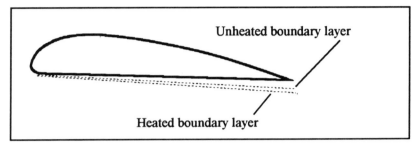

Figure 9.1 **Boundary layer heating increment**

Heating of the boundary layer would increase its thickness, and thereby increase the downwash angle of departing flow.

Because the downwash angle is determined in mergence of upper and lower surface flows of approximately equal mass rates, the net downwash angle addition would be half that of the lower surface flow. To evaluate the effect of this on lift we can use lift equation (2-2), in which we replace area, A, with the span-chord product, and since for small angles we can replace the sine with the angle in radians:

(9-1) $$\text{Lift} = \pi \rho v^2 \, SC \, \theta$$

Since lift is expressed as a linear function of downwash angle, we develop, in Appendix B, a formula for added lift due to boundary layer thermal expansion and its effect on downwash angle. Allowing for no losses, added lift becomes approximately:

(9-2) $$\text{Thermal lift} = \frac{2\pi vH}{Tc_p}$$

In the foregoing expression, H is the rate of heat input, v is airspeed, T is absolute ambient air temperature and c_p is the specific heat of air at constant temperature. Interestingly, effects of wing span, wing chord and boundary layer thickness cancel out in the derivation.

For an example flight situation let us assume the following:

1. Engine output is 150 horsepower.
2. Engine thermal efficiency is 30 percent.
3. Flight altitude is about 15,000 feet.
4. Ambient air Temperature is 40 F. or 500 R.
5. Airspeed is 140 knots, or 236 feet per second.
6. Air c_p is 7.7 btu per slug R°

From the engine horsepower and efficiency, we find the waste heat rate, h, to be 247 Btu per second. The lift then becomes:

$$\text{Thermal lift} = \frac{2 \times 3.14 \times 247 \text{ Btu/sec} \times 236 \text{ ft/second}}{500 \text{ degrees} \times 7.7 \text{ Btu per slug degree}}$$

$$= 95 \text{ pounds}$$

For the reader who prefers the metric system, we can recalculate lift in metric terms. The same conditions in metric are:

1. Engine power is 112 kilowatts.
2. Ambient air temperature is 278 degrees Kelvin.
3. Waste heat rate is 261 kilowatts
4. Airspeed is 72 meters per second
5. Air c_p is 1.0 Joule per Kg degree Kelvin

From this:

$$\text{Thermal lift} = \frac{2 \times 3.14 \times 261 \text{ Kw} \times 72 \text{ m/sec}}{278 \text{ K}° \times 1.0 \text{ Joule/}_{\text{Kg K}°}}$$

$$= 424 \text{ Newtons}$$
$$= 43 \text{ Kg wt. force}$$

This result of 95 pounds, or 43 Kilograms, is not negligible in comparison to airplane payload which might be around 1,000 pounds or 450 Kg, but we would have to consider added weight of the heat piping system. In the derivation we have included all waste heat of the engine, including the exhaust, which might not be feasible. However, on the other hand we have a cooling system which might have essentially no drag. Thus we might gain significant lift and eliminate parasitic cooling drag, as Darryl Phillips had imagined.

The real point of this thermal lift evaluation is to demonstrate that true understanding of flight principles in the aviation community could lead to innovation which might be beneficial. Evaluation of thermal lift feasibility with induction theory would have to begin with considering how heating the lower wing surface might influence the Kutta condition at a sharp trailing edge. This influence is not immediately obvious.

"Induced Drag"

The "induced drag" of induction theory begins with the fact that pressure above a wing is less than pressure beneath. We have considered lateral vortices generated from wing pressure difference as being centered about the wing tips and involving air recirculation upward from the entire below-wing region to the entire above-wing region, as was illustrated in Figure 6.4. Induction theory recognizes only small tip recirculation which creates a vortex core. This core is then said to *induce* the larger overall rotational movement with *induced downwash* over the wings, as illustrated in Figure 9.2.

Clearly, this is fiction. There is no known basis in physics for such induction. Furthermore, this concept denies the existence of overall air mass acceleration between below-wing and above-wing regions in response to pressure difference. This violates Newtonian physics laws which relate acceleration to applied force. Again, as we have seen in application of the Bernoulli theorem, there is reversal of cause and effect. Instead of vortices producing downwash, recirculation of downwash produces the vortices.

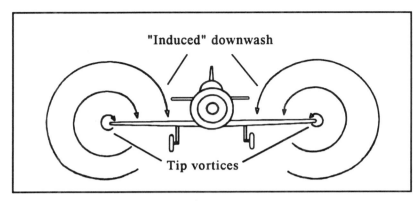

Figure 9.2 **Induced Downwash**

In induction theory, small vortices at the wing tips are said to "induce" larger circular movements including "induced downwash" over the wings.

As the wings are supposed to operate in the descending air of induced downwash, they are said to develop "induced drag." In effect, the wings are regarded as having to continuously climb to maintain altitude in this supposed descending air, but climb consumes power, and thus implies drag production. The drag is described as due to rearward tilt of the lift vector, caused by an *induced angle of attack*, as indicated in Figure 9.3.

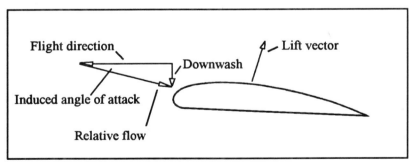

Figure 9.3 **Induced Angle of Attack**

According to classical circulation theory, downwash is induced at the wing by the trailing vortices, making the wing operate in descending air. The lift vector, perpendicular to passing flow, is said to be tilted rearward because of the *induced angle of attack*, related to direction of flow of passing air.

Because the air is supposed to be descending as a result of induction, and lift is defined as force perpendicular to wing travel in relation to the air, the lift force is defined as somewhat rearward. This rearward lift component is then said to be the source of induced drag. Thus induction theory attributes drag to the trailing vortices, as we did in recirculation theory, but through fictitious effects. It does not recognize drag associated with trailing vortices as due to lateral loss of downwash so that forward recirculation into recoverable upwash is attenuated.

Induction Theory Ground Effect

In induction theory, improved efficiency of the lift process when near the surface is attributed to *image vortices* beneath the surface, as indicated in Figure 9.4.

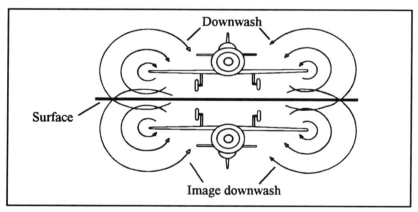

Figure 9.4 **Mirror Image in Ground Effect**

According to classical circulation theory, increased lift-to-drag ratio when operating near the surface can be analyzed as equivalent to having inverted vortex images reflected from the surface as if there were a second inverted airplane. Downwash induced by the image vortices are opposite in direction to downwash induced by vortices of the real airplane so that opposing induction effects reduce downwash at the airplane wings.

The image vortices concept is justified by saying that no downwash can pass the surface. Therefore the situation is as if an inverted image exists with induction effects which cancel the real downwash at the surface.

120

At the real airplane wing level, induction from the image vortices below would supposedly partially cancel the downwash induced by the real airplane tip vortices and thereby reduce the induced drag.

A problem with this concept, in addition to being mathematical fiction, is that inductive effects, if real, would interact not just on vertical air movement components between the wings, but on the more horizontal components of the circular patterns as well. It would appear that the greatest interaction would be where the patterns are nearest, in the lateral portions of air movement between the surface and the airplane wing. Here the effects would be additive in promoting rotational movement to cause increased "downwash." Thus this concept could be better used to explain reduction of lifting efficiency in ground effect if that were the case.

The Electromagnetic Loop

Induction theory includes a starting vortex, which is left behind a wing, a bound vortex of circulation which travels with the wing, and trailing vortices which extend from the wingtips rearward to join the starting vortex in a complete loop, as indicated below.

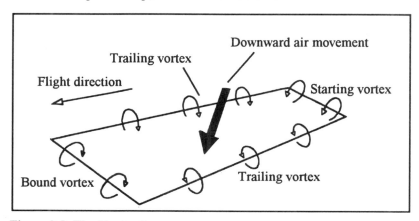

Figure 9.5 **The Vortex Loop**

Vortex theory includes a conceptual closed loop consisting of a starting vortex left behind, a bound vortex at the wing and trailing wingtip vortices between, all of which induce downward air movement through the loop.

Now compare the induction theory vortex loop to the electromagnetic loop of the next illustration.

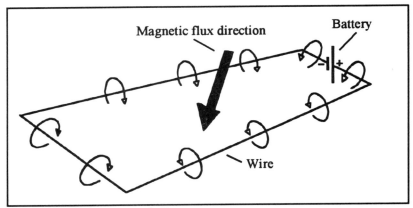

Figure 9.6 **Electromagnetic Loop**

Analogous to the starting vortex of the preceding illustration, the battery containing section of the magnetic loop initiates activity by passing electrical current through the loop. Each leg contributes to the magnetic flux which passes downward through the loop.

Electromagnetic Ground Effect

An interesting comparison between electromagnetism and aerodynamic induction theory is that of magnetic levitation to ground effect. When electrical superconductivity was becoming well known there were demonstrations on television of levitation of a permanent magnet above a superconducting surface. As the magnet was brought near the surface its field induced electrical currents in the surface. These induced currents then induced a counter-field which opposed that of the magnet with the result that the magnet could be left motionlessly suspended above the superconducting surface.

If instead of a permanent magnet, we were to have an electromagnetic loop as illustrated above, then opposite direction electric currents would be induced in the surface, and levitation would again occur, with elements comparable to the induction theory of ground effect. This is illustrated in Figure 9.7.

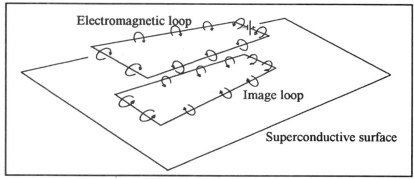

Figure 9.7 **Electromagnetic Levitation**

A current loop approaching a superconductive surface induces surface currents which produce magnetic fields repelling the loop. At a level where magnetic repulsion balances gravity, the loop will remain suspended.

Induction theory is based firmly on vortex theory, and assumes that behaviors of electromagnetic vortices and air vortices are essentially the same, but the assumption is not totally justified. Flexible electrical wires carrying strong currents in opposite directions can be seen to bow apart from mutual repulsion of oppositely rotating magnetic vortices. In contrast, oppositely rotating wingtip vortices can be seen to be attracted, as illustrated in Figure 9.8.

At airshows where wingtip vortices are made visible with smoke generators, the oppositely rotating vortices slowly drift together in some locations until they are within a few feet, and then quickly jump together at these locations to make smoke rings from the trails which had been continuous straight lines. The action indicates attraction force between the trails which varies inversely in relation to distance apart.

This difference in behavior suggests that other assumptions of vortex behavior in classical induction theory are also questionable. Certainly the concept of a starting vortex causing wing circulation is unjustified. Thus the idea that viscosity is necessary for lift initiation through starting vortex production is also without basis.

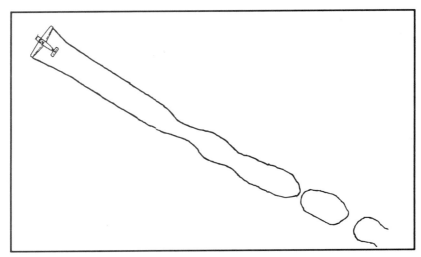

Figure 9.8 **Wingtip Vortices Breakup**

Wingtip vortices made visible by smoke generators tend to break into smoke rings as oppositely rotating sides converge in places influenced by air turbulence. The convergences tend to indicate that oppositely rotating air vortices are mutually attracted, rather than repulsed as are magnetic vortices of opposite directions.

The parallels between dynamics of air and dynamics of electromagnetism are interesting and perhaps worth studying, but it is apparent that vortex principles from electromagnetic theory are greatly over-extended in application to classical aerodynamics, while more appropriate explanations in terms of forces associated with accelerations of air mass are neglected.

A normal scientific process may involve observation of phenomena, forming a hypothesis to explain the phenomena, formulating a mathematical expression of the hypothesis, and then proving the hypothesis and mathematical expression by experiment. Unfortunately, in aerodynamics the process seems to have been perverted, beginning with mathematical expressions taken from electromagnetic theory to which unsound hypotheses have been tailored, even when the tailoring involved neglect of laws of physics. Students who are paying for, and working toward, becoming educated deserve more than to be taught these unsound concepts dressed in nice mathematics and represented as science.

124

Stop Abusing Bernoulli!
How Airplanes Really Fly

X. A GREAT NEW AGE FOR MANKIND?

Newton vs Bernoulli

It is interesting to visit aviation museums which have static displays or video presentations of how wings work. Most are based on hump theory, and some declare that lift is partially due to Newtonian reaction in downward acceleration of air, and partially due to upper surface pressure reduction in accordance with the Bernoulli theorem and the principle of equal transit times. Relative portions of lift attributed to pressure reduction and to downward acceleration of air mass differs between exhibits.

The concept of division of lift can be traced at least as far back as the Prandtl-Tietjens book copyrighted in 1934. In the book a calculation of pressure at the top and bottom of a square box, illustrated in Figure 10.1, is made on the basis of the Bernoulli theorem. The resulting lift is half that of real-world lift. Calculation of momentum passage difference through the vertical sides of the box again produces half. It is apparent that the two half-lifts can be added to arrive at the proper answer.

It appears that this exercise has led many in the several decades since to accept the idea that lift is partly due to pressure difference according to the Bernoulli theorem and partly due to Newtonian force of downward acceleration of air mass. In reality, the pressure effects at the top and bottom of the box are also due to Newtonian momentum effects in downward acceleration of air passing above and below the box. Thus all lift derives from Newtonian mass acceleration and reaction.

Any desired ratio of apparent pressure lift to momentum lift can be shown by choice of box height to width ratio. A tall, slender box will have relatively more area for momentum throughput and less for pressure action, or a short wide box would have relatively more upper and lower surface for pressure action and less sides area for momentum throughput.

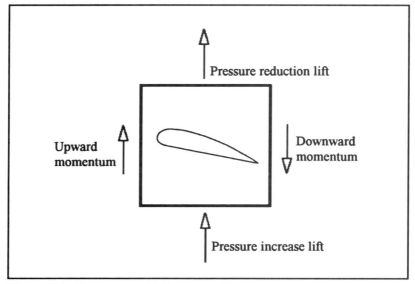

Figure 10.1 **Pressure and Momentum Box**

If the wing and center of circulation is located in an imaginary square box, through and around which air flow passes, then calculation of pressure difference between top and bottom in accordance with the Bernoulli theorem produces half the proper level of lift. If lift is calculated on a basis of Newtonian mass reaction in the change of vertical momentum of upwash entering the box and downwash departing, the result is again half the proper magnitude.

Defining lift proportions as resulting from independent actions of Bernoullian and Newtonian principles is a waste of mental effort. Pressure is exerted on passing air by the wing, causing air mass to accelerate in accordance with Newton's second law. In reaction, air mass resistance to acceleration produces counter pressure on the wing in accordance with Newton's third law. To distinguish between lift due to pressure difference and lift due to Newtonian principles of mass reaction is a bit incongruous.

All wing lift force is due to mass acceleration and reaction, and simultaneously all lift force is transmitted between the wing and passing air by pressure difference. Pressure and mass reaction effects are inseparable. The two act together in tandem, equally involved in the total lift.

A Truckload of Canaries

There is an old joke about a truck carrying canaries. Each time the truck approached a weigh station the driver would stop and beat the side of the truck with a club. When asked why, the driver replied that the truck was overloaded and he needed to frighten the canaries into flight so that they would not be supported by the truck and the truck would then weigh less.

There are many who believe that the birds' weights in flight would be supported by Bernoullian pressure reduction of their wings upper surfaces, and therefore the driver's idea was a good one. If only half of the weight were supported by wing upper surface pressure reduction, and the other half by downwash momentum production, as others believe, the idea would still be a good one.

A helicopter rotor is in fact a rotating wing. Anyone who has been near a helicopter in operation can testify that it does produce downwash. Thus we can conclude that rotor lift is at least partially in accordance with Newtonian principles of mass acceleration and reaction, but let us suppose that Bernoulli lift aside from downwash production is real. Then a helicopter could be built with a large fixed disk below the rotor to intercept downwash, and prevent it from disturbing the area over which it hovers. This would leave the Bernoulli lift (75 percent by some claims) operational even though downward momentum interception by the fixed disk would cancel out the 25 percent of lift due to downwash. The advantage would be that the helicopter would have no downward blast of air to disturb operations below, as for example during rescues.

Pollution Free Unlimited Energy

An even more important application could be achieved for space exploration. By totally enclosing a rotor in a large can, which would contain air, lift could be maintained even in the vacuum of outer space. Rotor downwash could be ducted back around the to the rotor input so that operation would be normal, as in ground effect. A large rotor would require a large container, but there is a solution.

Lift is proportional to fluid density. Mercury is about 11,000 times more dense than air so that a rotor operating in mercury would permit a very small thruster package size. If gimbals-mounted, thrust could be exerted in any direction for propelling air or surface transportation. Traction problems would be eliminated and vehicle design would be simplified

Such a thruster package would have great significance for mankind. Since the rotor would be totally enclosed with no reference to the outside world, thrust would be constant at any velocity of thruster movement. Its power delivery would equal thrust times its velocity of motion, even though rotor power input power would remain constant. In this there is potential for providing mankind with unlimited cheap electricity.

A mercury filled unit might produce 1000 pounds of thrust from 100 horsepower. A unit with drive mechanism and cooling radiator might have a diameter of one foot, and length of two feet. If we mount 100 of these units around a 75 ft. diameter wheel having its axis coupled to a motor-generator, the motor function could be used to start rotation , and then thruster power would drive the generator function. At 100 rpm wheel speed, the 100 units would produce 100,000 lb of thrust at 23,600 feet per minute. Power output would equal 71,000 horsepower minus drive power loss of 10,000 horsepower or 61,000 horsepower continuous output after starting, with no continued energy or fuel input.

Thermal power plants would become obsolete practically overnight. Electricity would become too cheap to meter. Localized plants would eliminate the need for transmission line towers. The threat of nuclear plant disaster would be eliminated, as would the pollution of fossil fuel plants. With power plants and all forms of surface, air and marine transportation powered by these thrusters, air pollution would become only a memory.

Of course, this is only possible if Newton's laws are wrong, and physicists will argue that this would be perpetual motion, violating the law of conservation of energy; but those who are fully convinced that Bernoulli effect lift production is possible without conformance to Newtonian principles should happily finance the promoters of this great new industry.

Stop Abusing Bernoulli!
How Airplanes Really Fly

APPENDIX A
THE LIFT EQUATION

An important consideration in lift calculation is that circulation velocity is inversely proportional to circulation radius. Thus if we can express circulation velocity at some radius, then we can express it at any other radius. We can start with Figure 11.1 where the vertical component of circulation velocity at the airfoil trailing edge is, in the manner of Newton, equal to incoming velocity times sine of the downwash angle, θ.

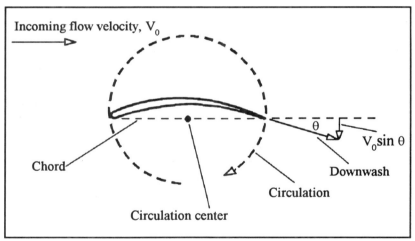

Figure 11.1 **Trailing Edge Downwash Vertical Component**

The airfoil above is of uniform curvature and has its circulation center at the middle of its chord, the line from leading edge to trailing edge. At low angles of deflection we may assume downwash velocity is equal in magnitude to incoming velocity, and the vertical component at the trailing edge is equal to incoming velocity times sine of the downwash angle. The vertical component at the trailing edge is tangent to, and thus equal to, circulation velocity.

Since circulation velocity is inversely proportional to radius, we can extend mathematical expression of circulation velocity components to any position in a plane tangent to the trailing edge, as shown in Figure 11.2. These components are defined as related to incoming flow velocity, airfoil chord and downwash angle.

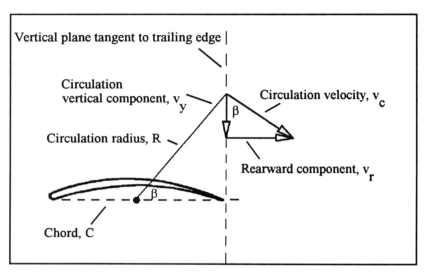

Figure 11.2 **Circulation Velocity Components in Trailing Edge Plane**

From (11-1) and the above, circulation components in a plane tangent to the trailing edge can be mathematically defined for use in lift calculation.

Circulation velocity at the trailing edge, equal to incoming velocity, v_0, times sine of the downwash angle, θ, is at a radius of one-half the chord length, or C/2. Since the velocity in circulation varies in inverse proportion to radius. Velocity of circulation at any radius, R, will be:

(11-1)
$$v_c = (v_0 \sin \theta) \left(\frac{C/2}{R} \right)$$

From the foregoing considerations, we can deduce rearward and vertical velocity components in a plane tangent to the trailing edge. Parameters for calculation of lift become:

130

$$v_c \text{ at trailing edge} = v_0 \sin \theta$$
$$v_c \text{ in aft plane} = (v_0 \sin \theta)(C/2)/R$$
$$v_y \text{ in aft plane} = (C/2)(v0 \sin \theta \cos \beta)/R$$
$$v_r \text{ in aft plane} = (C/2)(v_0 \sin \theta \sin \beta)/R$$

$$R = (C/2) \sec \beta$$
$$y = (C/2) \tan \beta$$
$$dy = (C/2) \sec^2\beta \; d\beta$$

In integrating the rate of downwash vertical momentum to determine lift due to downwash production, we shall use an imaginary vertical screen tangent to the airfoil trailing edge, as shown in Figure 11.3, through which all downwash passes.

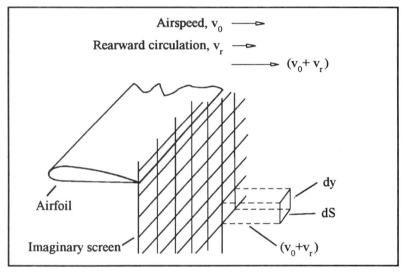

Figure 11.3 **Downwash Vertical Momentum Integration Screen**

The rearward-projecting block above represents screen opening area times rearward velocity of air passage through it. Volume of the block thus represents the volume rate of air passage through the screen opening. Associated with this volume rate is a downward momentum rate equal to the volume flow rate times air density times the vertical velocity component at that opening.

Length, $(v_0 + v_r)$, of the projecting block represents rearward air velocity through the screen opening. Multiplying this by vertical and spanwise dimensions, dy and dS, produces the rate of air passage through the opening, as represented by volume of the block.

Associated with the volume rate through the screen opening is vertical momentum density, equal to ρv_y, or the product of air mass density times the vertical component of velocity at the screen opening. Multiplying this vertical momentum density times the volume rate of air passage through the screen opening produces the rate of downward momentum passage through the opening, and the increment of lift associated with it.

$$\text{Screen opening lift increment} = \rho v_y \, (v_0 + v_r) \, ds \, dy$$

To obtain lift due to downwash passing through the entire imaginary screen, we integrate the lift contributions of all elements across the span, and to vertical distances of plus and minus infinity. After integrating across the span and separating the factors in parentheses above, the downwash lift integral becomes:

$$(11\text{-}2) \qquad L_{dw} = -\rho S \int_{-\infty}^{\infty} v_0 v_y \, dy \; - \rho S \int_{-\infty}^{\infty} v_r v_y \, dy$$

Substituting information from the preceding list:

$$(11\text{-}3) \quad L_{dw} = \frac{\rho v_0^2 \, SC \sin \theta}{2} \int_{-\pi/2}^{\pi/2} d\beta \; + \; \frac{\rho v_0^2 \, SC \sin^2 \theta}{2} \int_{-\pi/2}^{\pi/2} \sin \beta \cos \beta \, d\beta$$

which integrates to:

$$(11\text{-}4) \quad L_{dw} = \frac{\rho v_0^2 \, SC \sin \theta}{2} \; \beta \, \Big|_{-\pi/2}^{\pi/2} \; + \; \frac{\rho v_0^2 \, SC \sin^2 \theta}{4} \; \sin^2 \beta \, \Big|_{-\pi/2}^{\pi/2}$$

Here the second integral, which represents the effect of rearward circulation velocity on mass rate passage through the screen, reduces to zero as the effect of rearward circulation above the wing cancels out the effect of forward circulation below. After substituting area, A, for the span-chord product, SC, lift due to downwash evaluates as:

132

$$(11\text{-}5) \qquad \text{Downwash lift} \;=\; \frac{\pi \rho v_0{}^2 \; A \sin \theta}{2}$$

Here ρ is air density, v_0 is airspeed, A is airfoil area, and θ is downwash angle at the trailing edge. With no lateral recirculation loss, so that upwash momentum recovery is equal to downwash production, total lift would be twice that, or:

$$(11\text{-}6) \qquad \boxed{\text{Lift} = \pi \rho v_0{}^2 \; A \sin \theta}$$

This simple result, obtained by application of sound Newtonian principles, is equivalent to the lift equation of induction theory, but differs in being expressed as a function of trailing edge downwash angle rather than angle of attack. For an uncambered airfoil it doesn't matter, because the angle of trailing edge downwash would be equal to the angle of attack, as it was in the case of Newton's concept.

For a cambered airfoil, the downwash angle differs from the angle of attack by an amount equal to angle of attack at zero lift. This is normally a negative angle, as indicated in Figure 11.4.

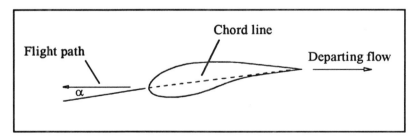

Figure 11.4 **Zero Lift Angle of Attack**

At zero lift angle where departing flow direction is parallel to the flight path, the angle of attack of a cambered airfoil is defined as negative because the chord line extension is angled downward in relation to the flight path or passing flow.

From the zero lift angle, repositioning would produce a theoretical downwash angle, θ, equal to the angle of attack increase. Thus the downwash angle of a cambered airfoil would equal the angle of attack minus the zero lift angle of attack, which is negative in the illustration, and lift would follow equation (11-7).

(11-7)
$$\boxed{\text{Lift} = \pi \rho v_0^2 \, A \sin (\alpha - \alpha_0)}$$

Here α is the angle of attack, and α_0 is the angle of attack at zero lift. The angle, $(\alpha - \alpha_0)$, is sometimes referred to as the *absolute angle of attack*.

Doubling the first part of expression (11-4), so as to include upwash recovery lift, and expressing the vertical range as something other than plus and minus infinity, lift due to a vertically limited portion of the air passage above and below the airfoil can be expressed as:

(11-8) $\quad$ Partial lift $= \rho v_0^2 \, A \sin \theta \, \arctan 2y/C \Big|_{y_1}^{y_2}$

If we evaluate lift associated with momentum passage through planes at leading and trailing edges to vertical distances of plus and minus one-half chord, we get lift due to momentum change in passage through a square box of chord dimensions containing the airfoil as:

(11-9) $\quad$ Square box momentum lift $= \rho v_0^2 \, A \sin \theta \, \arctan 2y/C \Big|_{-C/2}^{C/2}$

This evaluates as:

(11–10) Square box momentum lift $= \dfrac{\pi \rho \, v_0^2 \, A \sin \theta}{2}$

This is exactly half the proper level of lift, as Prandtl found (page 125). It is interesting to note that most of the lift is concentrated in momentum effects near the wing. If lift is evaluated as above to plus and minus four chord lengths vertically, the result is 92% of the proper level.

134

Stop Abusing Bernoulli!
How Airplanes Really Fly

APPENDIX B
THERMAL LIFT

Our purpose here is to evaluate the effect of downward acceleration of air passing beneath the wing as a result of heating and expansion in the boundary layer.

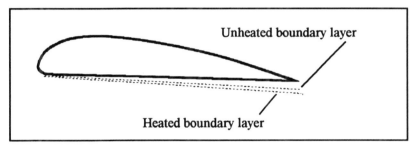

Figure 13.1 **Boundary layer heating increment**

Heating of the boundary layer would increase its thickness, and thereby increase the downwash angle of departing flow.

We begin with equation (9-1):

$$(9\text{-}1) \qquad\qquad \text{Lift} = \pi\rho v^2\, SC\, \theta$$

Since lift at low angles of downwash is a linear function of downwash angle, we can calculate the thermal increment of lift independently. To do this we need to replace θ above with the increment of angle due to heating.

Let us assume an initial thickness of boundary layer, b, which temperature increase, ΔT, causes to expand by an increment, Δb. It is this Δb which will produce an increase in downwash angle so as to produce added lift.

135

From the gas laws, the boundary layer will expand in proportion to its increase in absolute temperature:

$$(12\text{-}1) \qquad \frac{\Delta b}{b} = \frac{\Delta T}{T}$$

The temperature increase will be equal to the rate of heat input, H, divided by the capacity of the boundary layer to absorb it. The heat capacity rate, dc/dT, of the boundary layer will be equal to its mass flow rate, or volume rate times density, times the specific heat of air at constant pressure, c_p. If we assume a mean trailing edge boundary layer velocity of kv, proportional to airspeed, v, we can express the boundary layer mass flow rate in terms of wing span, S, times trailing edge boundary layer thickness, b, times speed, kv, times density, ρ. Thus the heat capacity rate becomes:

$$(12\text{-}2) \qquad dc/dT = Sbkv\rho c_p$$

The temperature rise then is equal to the heat input rate divided by the heat capacity rate:

$$(12\text{-}3) \qquad \Delta T = \frac{H}{Sbkv\rho c_p}$$

Substituting this into (13.1) to find Δb:

$$(12\text{-}4) \qquad \Delta b = \frac{H}{TSkv\rho c_p}$$

This Δb is downward thermal displacement of lower surface flow at the trailing edge. The downwash angle is due to combined upper and lower flows of approximately equal momentum rates. Thus the downward deflection of merging flow would be only half that above, but assuming the radius of circulation to be one-half of chord length, C, angular displacement of the downwash angle in radians would then be:

$$(12\text{-}5) \qquad \Delta\theta = \frac{H}{CTSkv\rho c_p}$$

Inserting the downwash angle increment into the lift equation yields:

$$(12\text{-}6) \qquad \text{Thermal lift} = (\pi\rho v^2 SC)\left(\frac{H}{Tk\rho vSC\, c_p}\right)$$

which reduces to:

$$(12\text{-}7) \qquad \text{Thermal lift} = \frac{\pi vH}{Tk\, c_p}$$

In this expression, v is airspeed, H is heat input rate, T is ambient absolute air temperature, c_p is the specific heat of air at constant temperature and k is the ratio of mean velocity of the boundary layer to airspeed. If we can assume the mean velocity of the boundary layer is half that of passing undisturbed flow, then the thermal lift becomes:

$$(12\text{-}8) \qquad \boxed{\text{Thermal Lift} = \frac{2\pi vH}{T\, c_p}}$$

This expression does not allow for trailing vortices loss.

Stop Abusing Bernoulli!
How Airplanes Really Fly

APPENDIX C
THE BERNOULLI THEOREM

We have not needed the Bernoulli in order to explain operation of wings or airplanes. However, the theorem is a useful tool for calculating pressure changes if velocity changes are known, or for calculating velocity changes if pressure changes are known. We shall briefly consider what the Bernoulli theorem is, some applications, and what it is not.

The Venturi Tube

The Venturi tube is an instrumentation device, named in honor of G.B. Venturi (1746-1822), an Italian physicist whose work led to its invention. A simple version of the tube is illustrated in Figure 13.1.

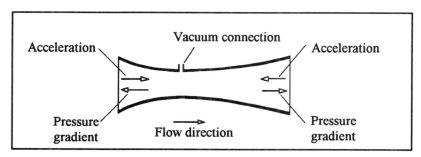

Figure 13.1 **Venturi Tube**

Instrument vacuum can be derived from a *Venturi tube*, mounted where it is exposed to passing air flow. Because of changing cross section area, air velocity relative to the tube increases from inlet to mid-tube, and decreases back to near inlet velocity at the exit. Pressure falls as relative velocity rises. At mid-tube where pressure is lowest, a vacuum connection is made. Pressure gradient vectors point in direction of higher pressure, while acceleration vectors point in direction of higher velocity. Note that acceleration and pressure gradient vectors point in opposite directions.

139

Initially, when a venturi tube is exposed to passing flow, there is impact pressure rise at the inlet because air mass within the tube resists acceleration. As air within the tube accelerates, the inlet pressure rise diminishes until finally, when flow has stabilized, pressure at inlet and outlet, except for viscous drag effects, is substantially equal to surrounding outside pressure.

The rate of mass flow through the tube is the same throughout its length. Therefore velocity must be greatest in the mid-section. Thus there must be rearward flow acceleration from the inlet to the smallest throat section, and there must be forward acceleration (or rearward deceleration) in the aft section from mid-throat rearward.

We shall regard the venturi tube air column as consisting of a stack of thin discs of air, one of which is represented in Figure 13.2. Pressure change at any point along the tube can be regarded as the sum of pressure changes produced by each disc element as these elements react to acceleration through the tube. As each element of air accelerates rearward toward the throat it produces forward force in reaction to the acceleration, in accordance with Newton's third law. As it decelerates aft of the throat it produces a rearward force. These forces, away from the throat, additively produce the throat pressure drop, for which we shall develop a mathematical expression based on Newtonian physics.

We shall consider the flow to be, for practical purposes, incompressible, as did Bernoulli, who developed his expression through consideration of essentially incompressible liquid, such as water. Thus the Bernoulli theorem applies well to flow of liquids, but when dealing with gases such as air there will be a some degree of inaccuracy due to compressibility.

We are dealing with relatively small pressure changes. Atmospheric pressure near sea level is around 14.7 pounds per square inch. In a venturi with an inlet velocity of 100 miles per hour and a throat velocity of 200 miles per hour, the throat pressure reduction would be about 0.44 psi, or three percent. Thus the effect of air density change due to expansion in the lower pressure would be small. In our development we shall disregard density variation.

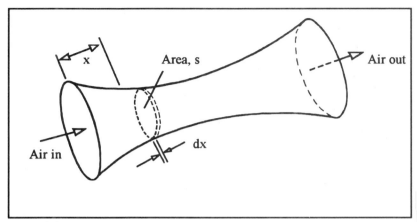

Figure 13.2 **Incremental Mass Elements**

Each imaginary element of air volume in the Venturi tube is of mass, dm, which is equal to the product of its cross section area, s, its length, dx, and density, ρ.

Each element of mass, dm, as it accelerates through the tube, opposes its acceleration with force of minus mass times acceleration, -(dm a). The force is distributed over surface area, s, so that the opposing increment of pressure becomes:

(13-1) $$dP = -\frac{dm\ a}{s}$$

Since dm is equal to the product, ρs dx, and a is equal to dv/dt:

(13-2) $$dP = -\rho\ dx\ \frac{dv}{dt}$$

And with $v = dx/dt$:

(13-3) $$dP = -\rho\ v\ dv$$

We can obtain total pressure change by adding up, or integrating, the pressure increments due to accelerating all the air mass elements filling space between the tube entry and any point of interest downstream. When (13-3) is integrated from the tube entrance to a downstream distance, x, the integral becomes:

$$(13\text{-}4) \qquad \Delta P = -\rho \int_{v_0}^{v_x} v \, dv$$

And after integrating:

$$(13\text{-}5) \qquad \Delta P = \frac{\rho(v_0^2 - v_x^2)}{2}$$

where ΔP is the pressure change, v_0 is entry velocity, and v_x is velocity at the point where the pressure change is taken.

Equation (13-5) provides pressure change accompanying velocity change. If flow of initial velocity, v_0, is stopped in impact with a fixed object, then v_x is equal to zero, and resultant pressure rise becomes:

$$(13\text{-}6) \qquad \Delta P = \frac{\rho v_0^2}{2}$$

This is a simplified version of the Bernoulli theorem. The theorem also contains other elements which for now are of no interest to us. From this, pressure rise potential in moving flow of velocity, v, known as *dynamic pressure*, can be expressed as:

$$(13\text{-}7) \qquad \text{Dynamic pressure} = \rho v^2/2$$

Pressure of air, P, as would be measured by a barometer unaffected by flow is known as *static pressure*. If the air is moving, it has potential for impact pressure rise to the sum of static pressure and dynamic pressure. This is known as *stagnation pressure*, or *total pressure*:

$$\text{Total pressure} = \text{Static pressure} + \text{Dynamic pressure}$$

or:

$$(13\text{-}8) \qquad \text{Total pressure} = P + \frac{\rho v^2}{2}$$

This total pressure represents energy content, which remains constant in the flow. Thus the above can be written as:

142

$$(13\text{-}9) \qquad P + \frac{\rho v^2}{2} = \text{Constant}$$

This is a more common form of the Bernoulli expression. It means that as pressure rises or falls, velocity squared must fall or rise in inverse proportion so that the sum of energy is unchanged. Likewise, pressure must change in inverse relation to change of velocity squared.

The preceding derivation demonstrates that the Bernoulli theorem derives from a pressure change calculation associated with acceleration. The theorem can also be derived from conservation of energy considerations.

In a pressure accumulator, the stored energy of a static quantity of incompressible fluid is equal to the product, PV, or pressure times volume. In addition, if the body of fluid is in motion, it has kinetic energy equal to its mass times velocity squared divided by two. If we add these to obtain total energy we get:

$$(13\text{-}10) \qquad PV + \frac{mv^2}{2} = \text{Total energy}$$

If the fluid is allowed to flow to a lower pressure without frictional losses, it develops kinetic energy equal to the reduction in PV energy. The total energy remains constant. Since mass, m, is equal to volume times density, if we divide the above by volume, V, we get:

$$(13\text{-}11) \qquad P + \frac{\rho v^2}{2} = \text{Energy per unit volume}$$

Which remains constant if the volume remains constant. Thus the Bernoulli theorem is merely a statement of conservation of energy for fluid in incompressible flow.

The Pitot Tube

Most airplanes rely on *pitot tubes* for critical airspeed information. Figure 13.3 shows a pitot tube which produces a pressure rise as it impacts upon air through which it travels. Air accelerated in impact on the tube rises in pressure in accordance with the Bernoulli theorem. Connected to the pitot tube, a pressure gage in the cockpit reads *indicated airspeed*.

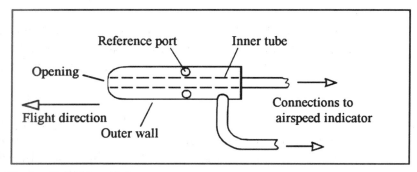

Figure 13.3 **Pitot Tube**

The Pitot tube usually consists of two concentric tubes having an annular space between them which is closed at front and rear. The inner tube at the forward end is open to air pressure produced by impacting air at the opening as it is accelerated to flight speed. The outer tube has vents at its wall so that the annular space is open to reference pressure of essentially unaccelerated air flowing by. Flow velocity can be measured as a function of inner tube pressure minus outer tube reference pressure. No flow exists in the connecting tubes to the indicator. The pressure difference is read on a differential gage calibrated in airspeed units.

Airplanes usually have static or reference ports located separately from pitot tube inlets, and away from the wing in order to reduce wing pressure difference effects. The ports may be located on the sides of the cabin as opposite pairs. Dual static ports, located on opposite sides, are common for safety in redundancy. Location of static ports can affect airspeed readings, as well as readings of altimeters which also connect to the static ports.

Because the airspeed indicator is calibrated for standard temperature and pressure at sea level, it is *advantageously inaccurate* in normal flight. It is more useful than would be an indicator of *true airspeed*. The critical time for needing meaningful airspeed indication is during takeoff and landing while near minimum flight speed. Because airplane performance is linked to the same factors of performance as the pitot tube, pitot-based airspeed indications are used for determining speeds for takeoff and landing and for other actions such as operating flaps and landing gear.

For the venturi tube with an air velocity doubling from 100 to 200 miles per hour, the change in pressure was about three percent. For the Pitot tube at 100 miles per hour it would be less, about one percent. Thus for most lightplanes a pitot tube airspeed indicator calibrated in accordance with the Bernoulli theorem will produce quite satisfactory results.

Bernoulli Theorem "Demonstrations"

The earlier section dealing with viscosity included a demonstration using a sheet of paper, usually presented as a demonstration of "Bernoulli effect," which was easily shown to be misleading. Another demonstration involves apparent attraction of the convex surface of a spoon into a falling stream of water from a faucet, as in Figure 13.4. It is usually claimed that pressure reduction at the spoon surface occurs due to velocity of the stream and the Bernoulli theorem, but in fact, force on the spoon is due to water being accelerated laterally as it wets and follows the spoon surface.

Wetting of the spoon, and surface tension of the water, excludes air from the spoon-water interface. The stream is then forced to follow the spoon convex surface so that it is deflected laterally. In being deflected, the stream develops an opposite-direction force which reduces pressure at the convex surface, in accordance with Newton's laws. Difference in pressures at the concave and convex surfaces then produces force on the spoon. If the spoon is reversed, so that its concave side contacts the falling water, it is forced away from the stream.

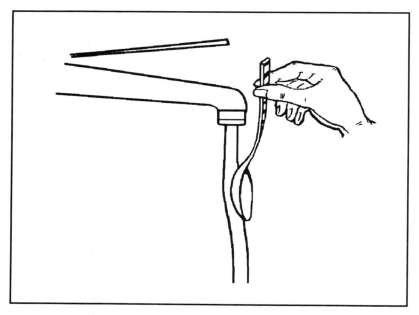

Figure 13.4 **"Bernoulli Effect" Demonstration**

A spoon held so that its convex surface is in contact with a falling stream of water seems to be drawn into the stream. Although this is used as a demonstration of "Bernoulli effect" due to velocity of the water, it is in reality only a demonstration of stream deflection due to wetting of the spoon and water surface tension.

If velocity alone were a cause of lowered pressure, then lowered pressure of the water stream would draw surrounding air into it, so that the stream would be continuously expanding after leaving the faucet, but velocity alone does not produce pressure drop. There must be acceleration of fluid mass.

Velocity is dependent upon point of reference. We live on a rotating planet which hurtles around the sun at high speed while the sun hurtles through the galaxy. The term "velocity" in regard to any moving bit of matter is meaningless except in relation to some point which is also moving. To simply say that velocity causes pressure decrease is not reasonable.

Another concept of lift recognizes velocity as a relative matter and says that pressure drop is a result of velocity in relation to a surface. Again this is false. If this were true, then an aircraft altimeter connected to static ports on the sides of a fuselage would have to be corrected for airspeed and resulting pressure drop at the ports. Otherwise airplanes of higher airspeeds but with identical altimeters would fly lower than slower airplanes, and air traffic separation would be a problem.

Spool and Paper Demonstration

Another demonstration, also usually regarded as one of "Bernoulli effect" involves a spool, such as used for sewing thread, a playing card or equivalent size piece of paper, and a thumb tack. The tack is pushed through the center of the card, and an end of the spool is placed in contact with the paper so that the tack projects into the hole of the spool.

If one blows into the other end of the spool, the paper clings to the end of the spool even when the spool axis is held vertical with the paper on the bottom.

At the spool inner edge, the flow path narrows in cross section from that of the center hole to a much smaller path as it enters the gap between spool and paper. The cross section area of flow path, equal to gap width times circumference at any radius, then increases with distance from the center. Thus, like a venturi, the flow path cross section area decreases and then increases as air passes from the spool center hole through the space between paper and spool.

At the outer edge of the spool pressure is atmospheric, and therefore conservation of energy principles dictate that pressure between outer and inner edges of the spool is less where the velocity is higher. Although this is in accordance with the Bernoulli theorem, it might be more appropriate to refer to it as a "venturi effect," since, like in the venturi, the pressure drops as the cross section of flow decreases from that of the center hole and then rises as the flow cross section increases with increasing radius from the center.

Although the spool demonstration conforms to what is thought of as "Bernoulli effect," it still follows Newton's laws. The pressure gradients involved are associated with accelerations of air mass.

Centrifugal Pressure Gradient

We have considered centrifugal pressure gradients in earlier sections where acceleration is centripetal, or inward toward the center of rotation. This is the basis of a centrifugal pump which operates by producing an outward pressure gradient, and higher pressure at the periphery where the outlet is located, or can produce lowered pressure at the center, as in a vacuum cleaner.

The centrifugal pump contains an impeller which rotates the pumped fluid within the pump housing to produce the desired effect. As an evaluation of the process, let us consider a rotating container, like a sealed fruit cake can, in which the fluid content has stabilized in angular velocity equaling that of the container, as indicated in Figure 13.5.

In centrifugal pressure calculation we shall consider an imaginary uniform column of air of length, r, extending from the container center to the outside wall. Cross section area of the column will be equal to s. Each increment of column length will equal dr. The mass, dm, of an element of air in the column will then equal the product of air density times volume, or: density, ρ, times area, s, times length, dr:

$$(13\text{-}12) \qquad\qquad dm = \rho s \, dr$$

As the mass element is accelerated inward with acceleration rate, a, it produces an outward force increment, dF, equal to mass times acceleration, or:

$$(13\text{-}13) \qquad\qquad dF = \rho s \, a \, dr$$

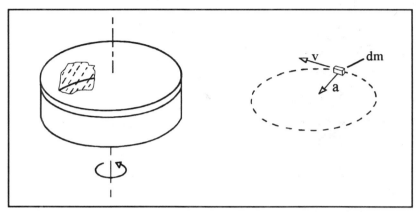

Figure 13.5 **Centrifugal Pressure Gradient**

As each bit of fluid mass, dm, in the container is forced to curve inward with acceleration, a, from its direction of velocity, v, it produces outward centrifugal reaction force which contributes to outward pressure acting against the container wall. Calculation of pressure rise in relation to radial distance involves integration of contributions of a series of tandem mass elements in a path along a radius from center to the outside wall.

When this force increment is distributed across the column cross section area, s, it produces a pressure increment, dp, equal to dF divided by s, or:

$$(13\text{-}14) \qquad dp = \rho a\, dr$$

From basic Newtonian physics, acceleration, a, in uniform circulation motion is equal to the square of radial velocity, ω, times radius, r, so that:

$$(13\text{-}15) \qquad dp = \rho \omega^2 r\, dr$$

Integrating pressure increments between two points along the radius, from r_1 to r_2, pressure rise, Δp, becomes:

$$(13\text{-}16) \qquad \Delta p = \rho\, (\omega^2 r_2^2 - \omega^2 r_1^2)/2$$

149

Since $\omega r = v$:

$$(13\text{-}17) \qquad\qquad \Delta p = \frac{\rho(v_2^2 - v_1^2)}{2}$$

With v_2 being the velocity of the container periphery, and velocity, v_1, at the center being zero, the pressure rise from center outward is:

$$(13\text{-}18) \qquad\qquad \Delta p = \frac{\rho\, v_2^2}{2}$$

Note that at first glance these last two equations appear to be more expressions of the Bernoulli theorem, in essence the same as expressions (13-5) and (13-6) for the venturi tube. However, in this case pressure increases with velocity rather than decreasing in accordance with the usual Bernoulli theorem expression.

The point to be made here is that it is not velocity which produces pressure change, but acceleration. Pressure change is a manifestation of mass reaction to acceleration in accordance with Newton's third law. The pressure gradient is always opposite in direction to the direction of acceleration. In rotation the acceleration is inward toward the center, and the pressure gradient, or direction of pressure rise is outward, away from the center.

It would be a mistake to say that in rotational flow the lowest pressure is always where velocity is lowest. In a vortex, or rotational movement comparable to a vortex such as a tornado, the lowest pressure is at the center, but highest velocities are also at or near the center.

Stop Abusing Bernoulli--
How Airplanes Really Fly
INDEX